MAN-MADE GEMSTONES

D. ELWELL

Center for Materials Research
Stanford University

D1555712

ELLIS HORWOOD LIMITED
Publishers   Chichester

Halsted Press: a division of
JOHN WILEY & SONS
New York - Chichester - Brisbane - Toronto

First published in 1979 by

ELLIS HORWOOD LIMITED

Market Cross House, Cooper Street, Chichester, West Sussex, PO19 1EB, England

The publisher's colophon is reproduced from James Gillison's drawing of the ancient Market Cross, Chichester

Distributors:

Australia, New Zealand, South-east Asia:
Jacaranda-Wiley Ltd., Jacaranda Press,
JOHN WILEY & SONS INC.,
G.P.O. Box 859, Brisbane, Queensland 40001, Australia.

Canada:
JOHN WILEY & SONS CANADA LIMITED
22 Worcester Road, Rexdale, Ontario, Canada.

Europe, Africa:
JOHN WILEY & SONS LIMITED
Baffins Lane, Chichester, West Sussex, England.

North and South America and the rest of the world:
HALSTED PRESS, a division of
JOHN WILEY & SONS
605 Third Avenue, New York, N.Y. 10016, U.S.A.

© 1979 Dennis Elwell/Ellis Horwood Ltd., Publishers

British Library Cataloguing in Publication Data
Elwell, Dennis
    Man-made gemstones.
    1. Precious stones, Artificial
    I. Title
    666'.88   TP873   78-41291

ISBN 0-85312-128-1 (Ellis Horwood Ltd., Publishers)
ISBN 0-470-26606-6 (Halsted Press)

Typeset in Press Roman by Ellis Horwood Ltd., Publishers
Printed in Great Britain by Cox & Wyman Ltd., Fakenham.

Frontispiece. A present fit for a Queen. Presentation made to H.M. Queen Elizabeth by Dr. W. Bardsley on the occasion of her visit to the Royal Signals and Radar Establishment, Malvern. Seven different materials grown in the laboratories (Britain's best known centre for crystal growth) are mounted in the form of a flower with petals in the shape of radar dishes.

MAN-MADE GEMSTONES

Table of Contents

This book is dedicated
to the memory of
my late father
Frank Elwell

Preface

This book is believed to be the first detailed account of the manufacture of man-made gemstones. It was suggested because there is no book dealing exclusively with the fascinating subject of how man's ingenuity can produce minerals which are as attractive as the products of nature, and frequently even more so.

The approach adopted by the author is partly historical and partly technological. The history of gem synthesis is considered an important feature and three historical aspects – the early history of faience and glass production, the development of the flame fusion furnace and the saga of attempts to make diamond – are described in detail. Modern methods of production are discussed in cases where the details are known, but it must be remembered that the major manufacturers often take considerable pains to safeguard the secrets of their processes. Nevertheless it is felt that readers who study the text should acquire sufficient information to be able to produce attractive gemstones in their own laboratory, factory or workshop.

The impact of scientific research and development on the gem scene has also been stressed at several points in the book. Science has generated a large number of attractive new materials which have greatly enhanced the choice of stones available to consumers. Usually these new materials, from rutile to cubic zirconia, are by-products of research in some totally unrelated field. In the fascinating example of opal, research into the structure of the natural material made possible the synthesis of gem opal, which was previously considered unlikely or impossible.

The study of gem synthesis is a natural interest for a crystal grower, because gems are the most attractive crystals grown – rather it should be said that the most attractive crystals are inevitably gemstones! This book was mainly written for the sort of people to whom the author has lectured over the years, especially amateur lapidarists who are always keen to discover the ways by which man-made gemstones are produced, as well as to inquire about properties and availability. The book should also be of interest to jewellers, who must deal with synthetic gems in their profession, and to anyone, technical or otherwise, seeking information on gems and their production. The level of writing is approximately that of *Scientific American* and no previous knowledge of the subject is assumed, but references are included for those seeking further information.

The chapters are written as fairly independent units, with only occasional cross-references. Chapter 1 is an account of the early history of production of imitation gems, mainly in Egypt, with a brief description of 19th century experiments which led eventually to the gem crystal growth industry. In the second Chapter the development of the first materials grown, corundums (such as ruby and sapphire) and spinels, is described with reference to flame fusion and to the range of more recent methods. Chapters 3–7 follow this pattern, each Chapter being devoted to a material or group of materials – emerald, diamond, the great variety of diamond simulants, the quartz family and opal, and the recent coloured synthetics. In each case the properties of the natural stone are considered so that the question of whether the man-made material is a true synthetic or not can be answered. Chapter 8 is a largely speculative account of what the future has in store, while Chapter 9 is a brief review of gem testing and factors governing the value of gems. Appendices contain data tables and a glossary, a bibliography, data on gem availability and a short introductory guide to ruby growth as a hobby.

This book was possible only with the help of a number of colleagues, producers and other specialists who provided information or illustrations. These are acknowledged in detail in the following Section.

DENNIS ELWELL.
Stanford University,
June 1978.

Acknowledgements

This book has benefitted from the information and illustrations provided by a number of individuals and organisations.

Particular thanks for photographs and diagrams are due to the following:

Frontispiece: Dr. W. Bardsley and colleagues at the Royal Signals and Radar Establishment, Malvern, England. (Copyright © Controller HMSO London, 1978); Fig. 1.3: British Museum; Fig. 1.6: Musee National d'Histoire Naturelle, Paris; Figs. 2.1 and 9.1: Dr. K. Nassau; Figs. 2.4–2.6: Mr. V. Djevahirdjian; Fig. 2.7: Dr. J. J. Rubin of Elvin Corp., NJ; Figs 3.2–3.4, 6.5 and 7.2–7.4, M. Pierre Gilson; Figs. 4.4, 4.7–4.9: Dr. R. H. Wentorf of General Electric, Schenectady; Fig. 4.6: Prof. H. Tracy Hall; Fig. 5.2, Mr. H. J. Scheel of the IBM Zurich Laboratory; Figs. 5.4–5.6: Mr. J. F. Wenckus of Ceres Corp., Waltham, MA; Fig. 6.1: Mr. D. R. Kinloch of Sawyer Research Products; Figs. 6.3, 6.4 and 6.7: Dr. J. V. Saunders of CSIRO, Melbourne, Australia. The author is especially grateful to Rosemarie Koch of the Center for Materials Research, Stanford University for the photographs of Figs. 2.9, 3.2–3.4, 6.2, 6.5, 7.2–7.4 and 8.1–8.3.

I am also grateful for the supply of information or specimens to: Dr. J. C. Angus, Case Western Reserve University; Carol A. R. Andrews, British Museum; Belgard & Frank Inc.: Mr. M. Bezalel; Dr. E. M. Comperchio, Synthetic Crystal Products Corp.; Mr. V. Djevahirdjian; Empreza de Couto Trading Co.; M. Pierre Gilson; Dr. M. B. Goatly, Royal Society; Prof. H. Tracy Hall; Dr. S. Iimori; Mr. W. E. Johnson, Morgan Hill, CA; Laser Technology Inc.; Mr. L. Merker, NL Industries; Mr. Y. Nakazumi; Dr. F. H. Pough; Mr. Leo Rigbey; Dr. K. Watanabe, Gunma University. Particular thanks are due to Mr. B. Sawyer, Dr. J. V. Saunders, Mr. J. L. Slocum, Mr. J. F. Wenckus and especially to

Stuart Samuelson (Deltronic Crystal Ind) and Larry Rothrock (Union Carbide) for their valuable help.

I also wish to express my gratitude to Dr. Eric White for introducing me to the study of synthetic gemstones and to Dr. John Robertson and Ron Murphy for helping me to develop this interest.

Finally thanks are due to my wife Jean who was my very skilful secretary during the preparation of the manuscript.

Introduction

The manufacture of gemstones is a fascinating and rewarding subject, and not only for those who produce or use these most beautiful of minerals.

The materials which will be described in this book are **synthetic** gemstones, the word 'synthetic' implying that they are synthesised from their chemical constituents. A truly synthetic version of a naturally-occurring gemstone has the same composition and therefore the same properties as the natural stone, apart from minor differences due to impurities. The book will also describe the many new gemstones which have no counterpart in nature and which have enriched the gem scene.

About the other kinds of man-made gemstones – **imitations** such as those made out of glass or by joining together different stones with a layer of colouring material and **treated** gemstones whose properties are changed by dyeing or irradiation – the book will have very little to say. The exceptions to this rule will include man's earliest attempts to produce alternatives to natural stones, particularly in ancient Egypt, which are important for their historical interest. A few examples of simulated materials from modern times are included also, where these are particularly interesting and attractive.

The terminology applied to man-made gemstones often causes confusion. A blue plastic made to look like turquoise is clearly an imitation, but what if the manufacturer uses poor quality natural turquoise, grinds it up, removes the most offensive objects, and bonds it together again with a small quantity of adhesive? It is obviously not a natural stone, although it is made from natural turquoise. Equally it is not a synthetic, since the adhesive is not present in the natural material. It is therefore an imitation. However, if the turquoise powder had been fused together by a suitable heat treatment (with no chemical changes) the material would be termed **reconstructed** (or **reconstituted**).

The International Confederation of Jewellery, Silverware, Diamonds, Pearls and Stones (CIBJO) take an extremely conservative view of all man-made gemstones, and even resent the use of the 'gem' as applied to man's products. According to their policy, genuine gemstones are those formed by nature without human intervention. A strict code is laid down for the description of the stone as it is displayed, for the very reasonable purpose of informing the consumer exactly what he is buying. According to this code, trade names like 'Superdiamond' (which I believe is my own invention!) are forbidden.

Clearly the code is not being applied at present because trade names are much in evidence, certainly in the United States. The rules may, however, be adopted as legally binding in the European Economic Community, so putting pressure on the legislators in the USA. These rules would presumably not be accepted without bitter legal battles by such manufacturers as Carroll F. Chatham, who won the right to refer to his emeralds as *cultured*, the same term used to describe pearls made by the 'seeding' of oysters. The point at issue is that 'synthetic' and 'artificial' have an unfortunate connotation liable to deter a would-be purchaser. Legal battles in the past have been long and interesting and, in this country where one adult male in every 125 is a lawyer, it may be expected that synthetic gemstones will provide plenty of litigation in the years ahead.

As a crystal grower, my sympathies are largely with the manufacturers and this book is mainly about their business and their products (and, occasionally, about their failures). I also have a healthy respect for the needs of the consumer, and would support legislation to make jewellers specify the nature of the stones they are offering. Finally, I reserve sympathy and respect for the jewellery trade and for the gem testing laboratories, to whom an apology is long overdue on behalf of the minority of persons with crystal growing skills who have set out to deceive.

CHAPTER 1

A Brief History

WHAT IS A GEMSTONE?

Gemstones are minerals which are highly valued for their beauty, durability and rarity and which may be worn for adornment or used to decorate art objects. It is not possible to say exactly what is meant by a gemstone and popular taste has varied over the years but any stone, down to a humble beach pebble, which can command a high price if attractively mounted in jewellery, could be considered a gemstone.

The visual appeal of different gemstones varies greatly. While most are highly transparent to light, others, such as moonstone or tiger's-eye, are translucent or cloudy in appearance, and a minority such as lapis lazuli, are opaque to light. The majority of gemstones are coloured, and it is the colour of many gems such as ruby, emerald, opal or alexandrite which is the most important feature and gives the stones their visual appeal. Colourless stones are also extremely popular, with diamond the outstanding example. The attractiveness of colourless stones depends mainly on two properties, known as **brilliance** and **fire**.

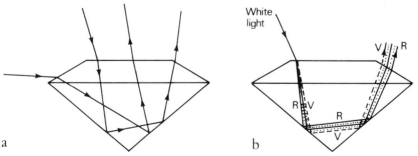

Fig. 1.1 (a) Brilliance depends on the ability of a crystal to reflect light to the eye. The higher the brilliance, the more the reflected light so that little light passes through the crystal. (b) Fire is the dispersion of white light into the colours of the spectrum (or rainbow). R indicates red light and V violet light.

Fire is the display of colour which can be seen when light is dispersed and shows us the colours of the spectrum displayed as through a prism, or through raindrops when they produce a rainbow. Brilliance is the ability of gems to gather light over a wide angle and to reflect it into the eye. This effect can be greatly enhanced by cutting the gemstone and displaying its myriad of small faces or **facets**, which are expertly cut at carefully selected angles. As a facetted stone is moved, light reaches the eye from continually changing facets, and the visual beauty of the gemstone will vary according to its brilliance and the interplay of its brilliance and fire. The attractiveness and value of the stone reaches its maximum only if the stone is a **single crystal**.

The concept of a single crystal may be a difficult one for the non-technical reader. If an 'atomic' microscope were available to look inside the crystal, it could be seen that the atoms are set in a regular array with a relatively simple arrangement of the atoms repeated from any edge of the crystal to the opposite edge. Corresponding to this symmetry, the external faces of the crystal (often called habit faces or natural facets) form simple angles, one to another, and so it is often possible to recognise a crystalline mineral from its external shape. Good examples of this characteristic shape from the gem kingdom are shown by **rock crystals**, colourless crystals of quartz originally found in the European Alps and which gave rise to the word 'crystal'. This word is derived from the Greek $\kappa\rho\tau\sigma\tau\alpha\lambda\lambda o\varsigma$ (*crystallos*) meaning 'ice', because it was believed that the rock crystals were a form of ice made from water which had frozen permanently on account of the extreme cold of the high mountains!

A minority of gemstones are not single crystals, and the most highly valued of this group is the opal, whose characteristics are described in Chapter 6. **Polycrystalline** materials contain internal boundaries between the tiny 'crystallites' which form the material, and these boundaries scatter the light so that the material becomes translucent or even opaque. This is why a crystal of quartz, which is perfectly transparent, will become a rather dull white powder if it is smashed with a hammer into very small pieces. Another example is chalk, an opaque form of calcium carbonate which may be perfectly transparent if it is produced in single crystal form, called **calcite** by geologists.

Glass is also transparent and is widely used in cheap jewellery. Glasses differ from single crystals in that the atoms are not arranged in a regular array, but our 'atomic microscope' would reveal a much more chaotic structure without the long-range regularity of crystalline materials. Because of this lack of regularity, glasses inevitably lack the brilliance of crystalline gemstones and cannot be compared with the single crystal form.

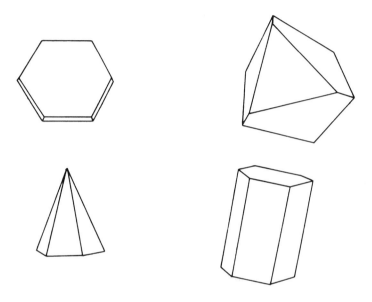

Fig. 1.2. Single crystals exhibit a characteristic habit, with distinct faces bounding the crystal. The diagram shows various possible forms of corundum crystals, including ruby and sapphire.

Only in single crystals can the facetting of the lapidarist be optimised as the facets on the gemstone are cut at angles which are related to the crystallographic characteristics of the material. All the transparent gemstones, including the 'precious stones' diamond, emerald, ruby and sapphire, are single crystals; and hence the skills required of the would-be manufacturer of these materials are those of the crystal grower. These same skills are used by industry to produce a wide range of crystals for an enormous variety of applications, many of which are described in the book by Arem [1] and by the books and journals in the academic discipline of crystal growth.

THE EARLY USE OF GEMS

The use of mineral and animal fragments, for adornment and as protection against evil spirits, has a very long history. The first use of jewellery probably began during the last Ice Age, sometime between 40,000 B.C. and 20,000 B.C. Carved figurines of women or animals found in Moravia in Central Europe have been given radio-carbon dates in the region of 25,000 B.C. and the carving of objects presumed to have religious significance played an important part in the life of the hunters of the late Palæolithic period. Cave-painting was also a part of the same culture and is probably better known, because the creations of the cave painter are more dramatic than the contemporary carvings or necklaces.

Early carvings were from serpentine, ivory, limestone, bone, haematite, antler and stone. Among the more attractive of the objects which have been discovered are the animal carvings in amber by the people of the Maglemose culture around the Baltic sea in Northern Europe. The carvings of bear, elk, deer and other animals are also interesting, not only because of the patterns formed by surface pricking but because of regular holes as well, probably produced by a bow drill [2].

The grave of a mammoth hunter of the Aurignacian period found in 1891 in Brno, Moravia, Czechoslovakia contained, in addition to a male figure carved from mammoth ivory, a long elaborate necklace of tusk. Shell bracelets and necklaces were found in other graves of the Aurignacian period, notably in a grave of two children at Menton in Southern France.

The development of jewellery essentially 'modern' in design began in Western Asia with the first civilizations of the Tigris-Euphrates valley in what is now mainly Iraq. The earliest item of jewellery in a 1976 exhibition 'Jewellery through 7000 Years' at the British Museum [3] was a necklace from Arpachiya, near Nineveh in Assyria, dated in the 'Halaf' period of about 5000 B.C. The necklace contained obsidian, a volcanic stone, together with cowrie shells, a bead of dark clay and a pendant of black stone. The clay bead was believed by its discoverers, M. E. L. Mallowan and J. C. Rose [4], to be an imitation of obsidian. This is probably the earliest known example of man's attempts to imitate the products of nature. The cowrie shells were originally filled with a red pigment – man's early attempt to improve upon nature. Red and black was a popular colour

combination of that period and was frequently used in contemporary
pottery.

Fig. 1.3. Necklace from Arpachiya in modern Iraq and dated from about 5000 B.C.
The necklace contains one imitation obsidian bead, made from clay, with cowrie
shells which were originally filled with a red pigment.

The Egyptian civilization closely followed the Mesopotamian and
their jewellery is rightfully regarded as providing the outstanding
examples of design and craftmanship of all pre-Christian era jewellery.
Most people are familiar with the very sophisticated jewellery found
in the Tutankhamun tomb, and many maintain that the beauty of
design and standard of craftsmanship of Egyptian jewellery of 4000
years ago has never been bettered. The Egyptians were highly skilled
goldsmiths and used turquoise, carnelian, lapis lazuli and other
stones in the manufacture of jewellery which often denoted social
rank in addition to serving a decorative purpose.

The sophisticated designs of the 18th Dynasty (1559-1353 B.C.)
clearly owed their origins to the primitive jewellery of the prehistoric
period. Stone beads were quite common in the so-called Badarian
period, when metals were known but when tools were still made of
stone [5]. The Badarians were farmers, living in primitive huts but
showing technical skills in their ivory carvings. They also used shells,
teeth, seeds, horns and bones, drilled and threaded on a string.

Further attempts to improve upon nature during this period have been observed, in the form of beads glazed with a blue colour derived from copper-containing minerals.

Gems were important items of trade from a remarkably early date, and trade routes became established as early as 5000 B.C. The Egyptians used turquoise mined in the Sinai peninsula, and they also imported emerald, and lapis lazuli from Afghanistan. The lapis mines at Badakshan and the turquoise mines in the Sinai are the oldest operating mines known. Lapis, the blue mineral specked with gold-coloured pyrites, is still obtained primarily from Afghanistan. The first scenes depicting jewellery makers date from the 4th Dynasty (about 2600 B.C.) from the tomb of Nebemakhet. They belonged to the artisan class, whose social standing is ranked between the scribes and the agricultural workers [6].

THE FIRST MAN-MADE GEMSTONES

It must be assumed that the supply of gem minerals, especially of the imported lapis lazuli, was not sufficient to meet the demand. The first attempt to solve this problem was the application of a glaze to an unattractive natural material, steatite, to make it resemble malachite or lapis. Steatite, which is a hydrated magnesium silicate, is a form of talc and is one of the softest natural minerals. It was found in Egypt at Gebel Fatira, less than 100 miles from el-Badari (after which the Badarian period is named), and is easy to carve or make into beads. Heating hardens the outside but does not melt the stone, so steatite is a good base for a glaze. A necklace excavated at Badari and dated around 4000 B.C. was made from green-glazed steatite, and a blue glaze was developed at about the same time. The earliest glazes were not truly vitreous but were made by forming a coloured paste and firing it onto the bead. The achievement of a really glazed bead became possible only as the technology developed to increase the firing temperatures, or alternatively by the addition of potash or some other material to lower the melting point of the glaze.

Attempts to produce beads resembling lapis lazuli have been described [7] as 'man's first move into the world of synthesising the mineral he required'. At a later stage, steatite was replaced by a man-made material obtained from powdered quartz and glazed to form the so-called **faience**, the beautiful material which enjoyed a long popularity for many centuries B.C. The technical details of faience production are not completely known, but considerable information has been accumulated from evidence from excavations, paintings and simulations. Faience production probably began in Mesopotamia around 4500 B.C. and a necklace containing faience beads and dated around 3000 B.C. was found by Sir Leonard Wooley at Ur ('Ur of the Chaldees') in Iraq. However it was in Egypt that the art of faience making reached its highest form.

Faience consists of 90–99% powdered quartz, produced by powdering quartz rocks, with the addition of oxides of aluminium, calcium, iron, magnesium, potassium and sodium. Quartz does not melt until it reaches a temperature of 1610°C, which is well beyond the capabilities of any early civilisation, but it softens above 1000° C and impure material could probably be compacted by heating at somewhat lower temperatures. Hodges [7] suggests a temperature of about 950°C, much hotter than a domestic fire and requiring some means of blowing air over heated charcoal. Initially the baba or faience maker used a papyrus reed tipped with a clay nozzle as a blowpipe, his furnace being a ceramic bowl on a stand filled with charcoal. Later, at the time of the New Kingdom (1559-1085 B.C.), leather bellows were invented as a means of producing the air flow, and firing took place in larger furnaces similar to those used for pottery. The firing temperature used by the Egyptians could not have exceeded 1100°C because the crucibles used to make glass (and presumably also for glazing) would have melted at this temperature [8]. A lidded crucible to keep out the smoke has been stated to be necessary for successful faience manufacture [7].

It is thought that the powdered quartz was mixed with water or some solution to form a paste which was probably roughly moulded into shape, mainly by hand [9]. Many thousands of moulds have been found for shaping beads, scarabs and other objects, some containing traces of the raw materials. Beads were made on a thread which was burnt out in the firing, except for larger beads which were pierced when soft with a pointed object [10].

The colour was applied by dipping the beads or other object into a glazing solution, which was allowed to dry prior to the second firing. The glaze consisted mainly of powdered silica but also contained about 25% of sodium and calcium carbonates, sometimes with a little potassium. The popular blue colour was caused by a copper

Fig. 1.4. (a) Early furnace used for pottery and presumably also for faience,
(from Beni Hasan).

(b) Later furnace design with higher temperatures produced by blowing air using
foot-operated bellows.

(c) Small furnace with blow-pipe and charcoal bowl.

compound which was ground up and added to the glazing solution too. Petrie [11] found evidence that the constituents were first partly fused to make a paste which was 'toasted' to get the required tint, then ground and added to water to form a paint which was mixed with a flux to form the glaze. Occasionally the colour was modified by the use of two layers of glazing.

It has not been established how glazing was first discovered. Petrie concluded that it was invented by finding quartz pebbles fluxed by wood ashes in a hot fire. Another possibility is that it was accidentally discovered during the smelting of copper, by finding glass in the residual slag from the furnaces: although it has also been proposed that copper smelting was an accidental discovery of faience making! In addition to plant ashes, the most likely source of the alkali metals needed to form a glass with silica at a moderate temperature was 'natron', mainly sodium carbonate and bicarbonate. Attempts to simulate the chance discovery of glazing have not been successful.

The majority of faience beads were blue or green because these resembled lapis lazuli and malachite, the most popular natural gem materials of the time [12]. Versatility with the use of colour was acquired in the Naqada II period (3500-3100 B.C.) and examples in the British Museum are clearly meant to imitate, among other minerals, olivine and green calcite in addition to lapis lazuli, malachite and turquoise [13]. White, red, violet, yellow and black beads were produced, and these same colours were used in complex shapes to form leaves or flowers. As the art of the faience maker reached its peak around 1500 B.C., beads in such elaborate shapes as lotus petals, cornflowers and willow leaves were mass-produced to make beautiful and elaborate collars [14]. The art of inlaying, for example of a coloured flower motif in a white faience terminal at each end of the collar, was also developed around this time.

The discovery of glazing would be expected to be followed closely by the use of glass beads as fashionable adornment, because the glazing material could also be used to make the beads. In spite of this, glass beads did not become common in Egypt until the 18th Dynasty, long after the first Badarian glaze. No good reason has been advanced for this long delay, which was apparently a matter of taste rather than of ability, because glass beads were found occasionally from earlier times.

The glass of ancient Egypt contained less silica and lime than modern glass, and more iron and aluminium oxides together with a higher level of minor impurities. It was made by mixing quartz sand, calcium carbonate, natron and colouring material, and was fired in a two-stage process. In the initial stage, the mix was converted to a 'frit' at about 750°, and this frit was converted to glass in clay crucibles at about 1000°–1100°C. The glass was colourless if no colouring element was added or was coloured purple (by manganese), black (iron), blue (cobalt), green (copper or iron), red (red copper oxide), or yellow (lead, possibly with antimony). The Egyptians considered colour more important than transparency and appeared to consider their manufactured faience or glass beads to be worthy of use alongside natural stones.

DEVELOPMENTS UP TO THE MIDDLE AGES

Jewellery was used extensively in other early civilizations: for example, several gems are mentioned in the Old and New Testaments of the Bible. The Greeks and Romans showed a general preference for decorated gold jewellery, with apparently little liking for gemstones, although engraved stones made into cameos were popular with the Romans, who were also the first to use diamonds. The so-called 'dark ages' produced some really beautiful jewellery, especially crosses, brooches and buckles set with a variety of stones. Jewellery has probably been a feature of all known civilizations and some notable styles were produced by, for example, the Aztecs in Mexico, the Inca in Peru, the Chinese of the Han Dynasty, and the Ashanti and their predecessors in West Africa. No notable new man-made gemstones appeared until relatively modern times.

Facetting of gemstones was introduced in Europe in the 16th Century and led slowly to a greater popularity of colourless stones, which are relatively dull when polished in the 'cabochon' cut without facets. The word 'cabochon' is derived from an early French word 'caboche' meaning 'head'. Although coloured and particularly red stones retained pride of place, diamonds became popular from about the 16th century, probably during the reign of Henry VIII.

During the Middle Ages gems were endowed with almost magical properties. In his splendid *Essay about the Origins and Virtues of Gems*, written in 1672, Robert Boyle [15] wrote, 'That the Scarcity, the Lustre and the Preciousness of Gems have made them in all ages to be reckon'd among the finest and choicest of Nature's Productions is generally granted'. Boyle was inclined to accept the general belief that gems could cure illness:

'For my part, I never saw any great feats perform'd by those hard and costly stones (as Diamonds, Rubies, Saphires) that are wont to be worn in Rings. But yet because Physicians have for so many Ages thought fit to receive the fragments of pretious stones into some of their most celebrated cordial compositions; because also divers eminent Men of that profession, some of them famous Writers, and some virtuosi of my own acquaintance, have by their Writings, or by word of Mouth, inform'd me of the very considerable effects of some Gems (especially Christal*) upon their own particular Observations . . . I will not immediately reject all the Medicinal Virtues that Tradition and the Writers about pretious Stones have ascribed to those Noble Minerals.'

Boyle believed that crushed gems in medicines might have some beneficial effect, by adding to the liquid traces of minerals, simulating the mineral 'waters' of Spas. This was a not unreasonable hypothesis. Boyle was one of the greatest chemists of his time, and was the first to recognise that gems form in nature from fluids and that the colour of gems could be due to traces of metal impurities. He performed the first characterisation of gems, measuring their density and hardness, and noting that ruby and sapphire have similar properties with the exception of their colour. Boyle also commented on the natural shape or 'habit' of crystals and advanced a theory that habit was due to a regular arrangement of 'corpuscles': another hypothesis not far from the truth. The *Essay* also contains descriptions of experiments to make gems; but in each case a solution in water was used, so that the 'gems' would not have been very durable.

The Middle Ages saw the growth of alchemy. It is quite possible that alchemists made attempts to grow precious stones from mixtures of minerals or chemicals heated in a furnace. Their language makes it difficult to decide, in many experiments, exactly what they did or were trying to accomplish, and no clear records of the genuine synthesis of gem materials have been preserved. Their main preoccupation was of course the transmutation of base metals into gold, but we can speculate that some attempts were made to produce rubies, diamonds, sapphires and other precious stones.

* Quartz

Fig. 1.5. The middle ages. This shows a pioneer French enamellist, Jean Toutin, firing an enamelled jewel in his furnace. The original drawing is dated 1610.

THE 19th CENTURY

The modern history of man-made gemstones began in 1837 when a French chemist, Marc A. Gaudin, melted together the two salts potash alum (potash aluminium sulphate) and potassium chromate, and prepared ruby crystals of nearly 1 carat (0.2g) in weight [16]. Gaudin's experiment followed a number of similar studies by mineralogists who had been attempting to reproduce or to simulate crystallization in rocks. The earliest of these experiments were performed in Britain by Hall [17] and Watt [18], who had studied the crystallization of lavas from the region around Edinburgh and from Mounts Etna and Vesuvius.

Gaudin's successful synthesis was repeated by a number of other French and German chemists, who experimented with different salts as solvents for ruby. The work around this time laid the foundation for the method of crystal growth which is now labelled **flux growth** or, by gemmologists, **flux fusion**. The general idea behind this method is to dissolve materials of high melting point in a solvent or 'flux' of much lower melting point. Crystals of the high-melting component are prepared by cooling the resulting solution or by allowing the solvent to evaporate, in the same way that crystals of copper sulphate are grown from solution in water. The growth of ruby crystals has only been possible from the prior knowledge that ruby consists of aluminium oxide, with a trace of chromium oxide which is responsible for the red colouration.

At the same time as attempts were in progress to evolve a method for growing large ruby crystals, J. Ebelmen was experimenting with the formation of emerald crystals. Ebelmen [19] dissolved poor quality emerald in molten boric oxide, B_2O_3, so his experiment was one of **recrystallization** rather than of **synthesis**, in other words the crystals were formed from their own constituent chemicals. Ebelmen's experiments failed to yield emeralds of gem quality, and the first successful synthesis of emerald had to wait 40 years. It was in 1888 that P. Hautefeuille and A. Perrey [20] introduced new solvents for crystal growth of emerald, namely lithium molybdate $Li_2Mo_2O_7$ and lithium vanadate $LiVO_3$. Although the emerald crystals were very small, a modification of their method was successfully employed in the commercial production of gem emerald and is described in Chapter 3.

The early experimenters often made use of furnaces in large industrial factories. Electrical power for furnaces was a novelty in a time when gas or solid-fuel were more commonly in use. Ebelmen's experiments, for example, were performed in the famous French porcelain factory at Sèvres, and a glass factory at St. Gobain was the site of another famous series of experiments by Edmond Frémy and his students. Frémy concentrated on ruby, 'perhaps the mineral which has most exercised the sagacity of chemists.' In 1877, Frémy and Feil [21] described an experiment in which they heated a solution of 20-30 kg containing aluminium oxide in lead oxide for 20 days in a large porcelain vessel. Crystallization resulted from a combination of solvent evaporation and chemical reaction with the crucible walls and with the furnace gases such as water vapour. The crystals made by Frémy were very small in spite of the large melts sometimes used, mainly because of poor control of the furnace temperature. Nassau and Nassau [22] have reported that one experiment with a 12-litre crucible yielded as many as 24,000 crystals weighing 1200 g in total. Frémy's crystals have been preserved and displayed at the Museum of Natural History in Paris: although related attempts continued into the 20th Century, these experimenters never succeeded in solving the problem of restricting the number of crystals which nucleated. The rubies they produced were too small and the cost too high for them to be a commercial threat to natural rubies, although some were set into jewelllery. The bulk of Frémy's experiments are described in a book *Synthèse du rubis*, published in 1891.

Fig. 1.6. Photograph showing ruby crystals lining the furnace of Frémy's furnace (late 19th century)

The factor which eventually led to the temporary loss of interest in the flux method was the development of a more successful alternative technique involving use of the flame fusion method. Around 1886 there appeared on the market a new type of ruby crystal of better shape and quality than Frémy's. These were given the name of 'Geneva' ruby, and although their precise origin and method of manufacture have remained a mystery it has been widely reported that they were made by an 'enterprising priest': certainly they appear to have been marketed with great success. These rubies were believed until very recently to have been 'reconstructed' by fusing together small lumps of ruby, but Nassau [23] has shown that they were more probably prepared by fusion of powder in a simple gas-oxygen burner.

The success of the Geneva ruby particularly impressed one of Frémy's students, Auguste Verneuil, who began a series of experiments on the crystallization of ruby by the **flame fusion** process, without the use of a flux. By 1891, Verneuil had developed a new and very successful coal gas-oxygen or hydrogen-oxygen furnace capable of reaching the 2050°C required to melt ruby, and produced ruby crystals superior to the 'Geneva' material. Although the details of Verneuil's 'chalumeau' were not published until 1904, his work laid the firm foundation for the successful commercial production of gemstones in large quantities.

REFERENCES

[1] J. L. Arem, *Man-Made Crystals*, Smithsonian Press, Washington, 1973.
[2] T. G. E. Powell, *Prehistoric Art*, Thames & Hudson, London, 1966.
[3] *Jewellery through 7000 Years*, British Museum Publications, London, 1976.
[4] M. E. L. Mallowan and J. C. Rose, *Excavations at Tall Arpachiya,* 1933, Iraq II (1935).
[5] M. A. Murray, *The Splendour that was Egypt*, Sidgwick and Jackson, London, 1963.
[6] A. Wilkinson, *Ancient Egyptian Jewellery*, Methuen, London, 1971.
[7] H. Hodges, *Technology in the Ancient World*, Penguin, London, 1970.
[8] W. E. S. Turner, *Journal of the Society of Glass Technology*, 38 (1952), 436.
[9] A. Lucas and J. R. Harris, *Ancient Egyptian Materials & Industries, 4th Edition*, Edward Arnold, London, 1962.
[10] G. A. Reisner, *Excavations at Kerma*, IV-V, Harvard University Press, 1923.

[11] W. M. F. Petrie, *Arts and Crafts of Ancient Egypt*, T. N. Foulis, London, 1910.

[12] A. Erman, *Life in Ancient Egypt*, Macmillan, London, 1894.

[13] C. A. R. Andrews (British Museum) private communication.

[14] C. Aldred, *Jewels of the Pharaohs*, Thames & Hudson, London, 1971.

[15] R. Boyle, *An Essay about the Origins and Virtues of Gems*, 1672, reprinted by Hafner, New York, 1972.

[16] M. A. Gaudin, *Comptes Rendus Acad. Sci. Paris*, **4** (1837), 999.

[17] J. Hall, *Edinburgh Roy. Soc. Trans.*, **5** (1805) 8, 56.

[18] G. Watt, *Phil. Trans.*, (1804) 279.

[19] J. Ebelmen, *Ann. Chim. Phys.*, (3) 22 (1848) 211, 213.

[20] P. Hautefeuille and A. Perrey, *Comptes Rendus Acad. Sci. Paris*, **106** (1888), 1800.

[21] E. Frémy and C. Feil, *Comptes Rendus Acad. Sci. Paris*, **106** (1888), 565.

[22] K. Nassau and J. Nassau, *Lapidary Journal*, **24** (1971) 1284.

[23] K. Nassau, *Journal of Crystal Growth*, **5** (1969), 338.

CHAPTER 2

Ruby, Sapphire and Spinel

Ruby and sapphire, although very different in appearance, are identical in crystal structure and properties except for those elements, present in small concentrations, which give them their characteristic colours. It was Robert Boyle who in 1672 remarked that, 'the degree of hardness of rubies and sapphires is so equal that a jeweller takes them to be the same stone except for colour', and he confirmed this by showing that they have the same density [1]. Chemically speaking, ruby and sapphire are mainly composed of aluminium oxide, Al_2O_3, the crystalline form of which is called **corundum** by mineralogists. Confusion is caused by the use of the name **alumina** to refer to the same material, but alumina is an abbreviation for all forms of aluminium oxide while corundum refers only to the crystalline material. Pure corundum is colourless and colourless corundum is found in nature, and is called 'white sapphire' by gemmologists. Although most people think of sapphire as a blue gemstone, it can exist in a variety of colours, yellow, pink, orange and blue-green in addition to the colourless variety. Ruby is strictly 'red sapphire' but its name originated long before the similarity between its properties and those of sapphire were noted. The characteristic colour of ruby is caused by the presence of the element chromium. The colour may be modified by the presence of other impurities, the most highly prized shade being said to be the colour of 'pigeon's blood', although presumably jewellers are not in the habit of cutting open pigeons to see whether their stones match up with this ideal!

All forms of corundum are hard, and this hardness together with the superb colours has led to the great popularity of ruby and sapphire for rings and other jewellery. Corundum is also the material most widely used for bearings in various instruments, including the 'jewels' of the watchmaker.

GENEVA RUBIES

As mentioned in the last Chapter, small ruby crystals had been synthesized by Gaudin and by Frémy and Feil, but the stones which really shook the jewellery 'establishment' of the time were the so-called Geneva rubies. These stones were first reported in 1886 by P. M. E. Jannettaz, a mineralogist at the Museum of Natural History in Paris [2]. Although the stones had initially been accepted as natural rubies, a group of jewellers had become suspicious and had taken a sample of the stones to Jannettaz for his opinion. Jannettaz consulted Prof. M. Friedel of the Sorbonne University and M. Vanderhym, President of the Syndicate of Diamonds and Precious Stones, and all agreed that the rubies were synthetic. The vital clue was a number of tiny bubbles present in the crystals. These bubbles are commonly present when crystals are grown by melting in a high temperature flame. Although natural crystals may contain inclusions of liquids, solids and even gases they never exhibit the arrays of tiny gas bubbles which are characteristic of production in the flames obtained by burning either hydrogen or coal gas with oxygen.

The difficulty experienced by the jewellery trade in identifying the rubies as synthetic is illustrated in this report from a trade paper of 1890, quoted by Robert Webster in his classic book *Gems* [3]:

'A Berlin jeweller has just been the victim of a curious hoax. He recently received a circular from a Zurich firm offering rubies at remarkably cheap rates, and therefore entered into negotiations for the purchase of some. He bought 25 rubies for which he paid 4,500 marks (then £225), receiving a guarantee from the firm that the stones were genuine. Shortly after, the jeweller heard that false rubies were being manufactured so cleverly as to decieve the connoiseur, and, being alarmed, sent those he had purchased to Paris to be examined by the Syndicate of Dealers in Precious Stones, who were considered unimpeachable authorities. They reported that the stones were not imitation, but were real rubies, which were small and consequently of little value, fastened together so cleverly as to render detection difficult. The jeweller wrote to Zurich resquesting the firm to take back the stones. This they refused to do on the ground that their guarantee only ensured the genuineness of the gems and contained no mention of their size.'

So began the legend that the Geneva rubies were 'reconstructed' from very small natural rubies.

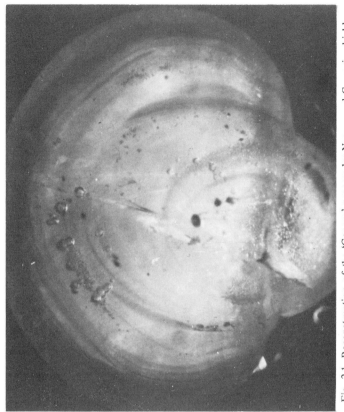

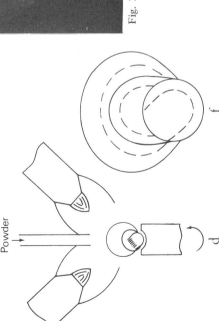

Fig. 2.1. Reconstruction of the 'Geneva' process by Nassau and Crowningshield.
(a) Melting the tip of a cone of ruby powder.
(b) Removal and inversion of the molten region.
(c) Formation of second globule.
(d) Addition of powder with two torches to form the third region.
(e) Photograph of a 'Geneva' ruby section.
(f) Drawing showing the three growth regions.

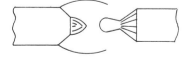

This assumption that the Geneva rubies were somehow constituted of fragments of natural crystals fused together was accepted by gemmologists until 1969, when Kurt Nassau of the Bell Laboratories, New Jersey and Robert Crowningshield of the Gemmological Institute of America in New York reported their study of the Geneva Process [4]. The conclusion was that a method involving the fusing together of tiny crystals could not have produced transparent rubies. In fact the process used powdered material and gas torches, employed in a rather complex three stage procedure. In the first stage, a flame was played on a mound of ruby powder to melt a small blob on the top. This molten region was then removed and inverted in a hemispherical recess, and the flame was played on the new upper surface to form a roughly spherical globule, slightly larger in diameter than the first. Powdered material was then added progressively to the top of this globule, with two torches providing the necessary heat to cause the crystal to grow. The flames were applied from the side with the torches either horizontal or inclined at a small angle to the vertical, sufficient to permit the insertion of a tube down which the powder was added.

The Nassau-Crowningshield reconstruction of the Geneva process was based on several factors, particularly on an analysis of the chromium content in various regions of the crystal. This clearly showed the presence of three separate regions within the specimen. Using the method proposed they were able to produce crystals very similar to those known to have been made by the Geneva process, whereas attempts at 'reconstruction' using small chips of natural ruby yielded stones which had a polycrystalline grey boundary between the individual ruby chips. Other evidence supporting the Nassau-Crowningshield re-creation of the Geneva process was a description given in 1953 to Dr. Eduard Gubelin of Lucerne, Switzerland by a Mr. Busser, who claimed to have grown Geneva rubies in his youth. Busser's account mentioned a multi-step process, multiple torches, rotation of the crystal and the use of a platinum tube [4]. The relative complexity of the the process was made necessary by the problem of avoiding cracking of the rubies.

AUGUSTE VERNEUIL

Whether this process was known in broad terms to Auguste Verneuil is uncertain, but he was aware of attempts by Marc A.

Gaudin in France to prepare ruby crystals using oxy-hydrogen torches. In 1869 Gaudin [5] presented to the Academy of Sciences in Paris a small collection of gems, based on corundum, which he had prepared with his oxy-hydrogen 'chalumeau', the word subsequently used by Verneuil to describe his own torch. Gaudin's collection included a blue sapphire, an 'emerald', a 'topaz', a clear stone 'imitating diamond' and a 'peridot'. To improve the free-flowing property of his alumina powder Gaudin found it necessary to add a high proportion of silica SiO_2, and because silica encourages the formation of a glass rather than a crystalline material he feared that his products were glasses. The apparatus available at that time was not sufficiently developed to distinguish between a crystal and a glass, and it is not certain whether or not Gaudin did make sapphire crystals.

    Verneuil concentrated his efforts on improving the flame-fusion

Fig. 2.2. Auguste Verneuil.

process and by 1891 had made sufficient progress to deposit details of his new apparatus and procedure with the Academy of Sciences. The aim of obtaining fairly large crystals was apparently realised at this stage, but trouble was experienced with cracking of the crystals. This problem was solved shortly afterwards by reducing the area of contact between the crystal and its support. A second sealed note to this effect was deposited with the Paris Academy, although the contents of both notes were not known until 1910, when they were opened at Verneuil's request [6].

The crystals grown by Verneuil's process were known as **boules**, apparently because the early crystals were roughly of spherical shape ('Boules' is more widely used to describe a popular French game in which heavy spheres about 10 cm in diameter are thrown to land close to a target). This term, introduced by Gaudin (as 'bulles') and used by Verneuil, has now become part of the terminology of crystal growth and of gemmology, although the crystals now grown by the flame fusion method are usually cylindrical.

In 1900 Verneuil's assistant Marc Pacquier exhibited rubies at the Paris World Fair. A report on the stones was written by the gemmologist I. Friedlander, who concluded that the rubies had been prepared by a new process and not by the Geneva technique. No details of the process were released until 1902 [7], but there was great demand for the rubies at the Paris exhibition [6].

Verneuil introduced his first brief report, published two years later, by stating that Gaudin had used too high a temperature, which made his crystals opaque. The new concept was that of a vertical torch, with the powdered alumina introduced into the flame through a stream of oxygen gas. The powder is shaken into the gas flow by the action of an electrically-driven vibrator. A gas-tight rubber collar supports the vessel containing the alumina powder, and allows the shocks from the vibrator to be transmitted without leakage of the oxygen. A ceramic pedestal is located in the cooler region of the flame and receives the tiny droplets of liquid alumina which are formed as the powder melts on passing through the hotter region. The flame is surrounded by a ceramic screen which acts as an insulator and shields the growing boule from draughts. This screen is provided with an observation window, which in Verneuil's original apparatus was made of mica. A water jacket protects the upper part of the apparatus from excessive heating due to the flow of heat from the hot zone.

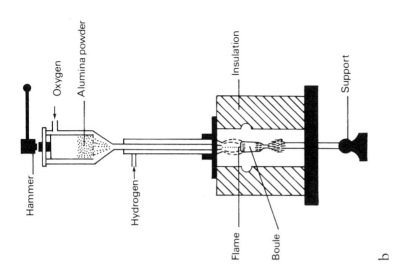

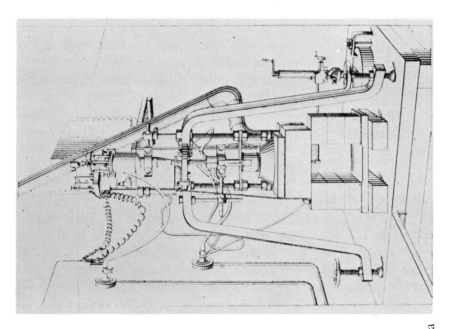

Fig. 2.3. (a) Original drawing of Verneuil's apparatus for the growth of ruby by
the flame-fusion method.
(b) Diagram showing the principle of the flame fusion furnace.

In the initial stage of a boule's growth, the powder solidifies on reaching the pedestal and builds up a cone of relative low density. Eventually the cone reaches a part of the flame sufficiently hot for the tip to melt. Several small crystals tend to form at this stage, but the one which is oriented in the direction of most rapid growth develops at the expense of the others and so provides the 'seed' from which the boule develops. Operator skill is particularly important during the early stage of growth while this selection process occurs and some adjustment may be made to the flame temperature or to the rate of flow of powder. Once a single crystal has become the dominant growth centre, to increase the diameter of the boule the powder feed-rate is increased and the flame temperature is gradually raised by adjustment of the oxygen flow rate. The top surface of the boule becomes a hemisphere to which fresh alumina is added as the molten droplets fall onto it. Lowering of the pedestal is begun to match the rate at which the boule grows.

The most important condition for the growth of high quality crystals is that the powder flow must be smooth, and much effort has been devoted to the preparation of feed material with good flow characteristics. If the powder is too coarse, the local cooling produced as a cool solid particle strikes the thin molten zone may cause it to solidify. Then many tiny crystals will nucleate at that point so that the boule will lose its single crystal structure. Too fine a particle size leads to evaporation of alumina in the flame. The optimum particle size is in the sub-micron range (below a thousandth of a mm) and the particles must be of regular shape so that they respond evenly to the action of the vibrator. Verneuil made his alumina by heating ammonium alum, containing about 2½% of chrome alum to provide the chromium to give the stone its red colour. This powder was heated to decompose it and yield the oxides, and was ground and sieved through a wire mesh to give the required particle size.

Verneuil grew ruby boules weighing 2½-3 g (12-15 carat) in about 2 hours. The boules were roughly spherical in shape and some were 5-6 mm in diameter. A more detailed description of his process was published [8] in 1904, with drawings of the apparatus. This apparatus, together with examples of the earliest crystals grown, is now exhibited at the Conservatoire des Arts et Métiers in Paris. Verneuil experienced problems with the vibrator which shook the powder into the oxygen stream, and later replaced it with a hammer worked by a motor. This simple and robust arrangement has been preferred in most contemporary apparatus used for commercial production.

From his description, it seems that Verneuil was generally pleased with the quality of his rubies, which showed a 'magnifique' red fluorescence, had the same hardness as the natural stones and were capable of taking a high polish. He did not acknowledge, however, that the synthetic rubies could be distinguished from the natural stones by variations in the intensity of the colour and by the gas bubbles which were present if the oxygen content of the flame was not kept fairly low.

After the 1904 publication, Verneuil turned his attention to sapphire. At that time it was not known which element was responsible for the blue colour of sapphire, but Verneuil was able to show that a combination of iron oxide and titanium oxide gave the same colour as the natural stone [9]. During this period, Verneuil acted as consultant to the firm of L. Heller and Son of New York and Paris. His sapphires were obtained by adding 1.5% of iron oxide and 0.5% of titanium oxide in place of the chromium oxide used in the ruby. The origin within the crystal of the blue colour is due to a rather complex mechanism. Colour in gemstones is normally associated with the absorption of light at characteristic wavelengths by certain elements, especially to so-called transition elements like iron, cobalt, nickel and chromium. When a band of colours is removed from white light, the light reflected to the eye is coloured with the **complementary** colour. For example, the red colour of ruby arises because chromium in the corundum crystal lattice absorbs green light selectively. The blue of sapphire requires the absorption of yellow-orange light, and this absorption occurs when electrons 'jump' within the crystal from an iron atom to a titanium atom. Therefore both iron and titanium must be present if the required blue colour is to be produced.

Patents for the growth of sapphire were published in 1911, the later one referring to bubble-like spots, curved growth lines and cracks as characteristic features of the synthetic sapphires [10]. In 1913 the annual rate of production of sapphire was already 6 million carats (1200 kg) and that of ruby 10 million carats (2000 kg). Verneuil, who made this production possible, died on April 13th of that year at the age of 57.

DJEVA

The production of sapphire and ruby was taken up by several

companies, most successfully by Hrand Djevahirdjian, who had previously been engaged in the manufacture of 'Geneva' type ruby in Paris. Djevahirdjian saw the advantages of the Verneuil furnace and began to use this method as early as 1903. In 1905 he moved production to a larger workshop at Villeurbanne, near Lyon, and then to a factory at Arudy in the Low Pyrenees. In 1914 there was a further move to the present site of the company at Monthey near Lake Geneva in Switzerland. Vital factors in the cost of production by the flame fusion process are oxygen and hydrogen for the furnaces, and from the start the firm now known as 'Djeva' gave close attention to economic production of these gases. From the early years of gem synthesis, oxygen and hydrogen were produced on site by conventional methods and sold as by-products. In 1948 the company installed plants for the production of the gases by electrolysis of water. Sources of cheap electricity are vital if oxygen and hydrogen

Fig. 2.4. Hrand Djevahirdjian.

Fig. 2.5. (a) A line of production furnaces from the Djeva factory in Monthey,
Switzerland.
(b) Interior of a flame fusion furnace used for ruby production.

are to be produced at an economic price, and a site in the foothills of the Alps with cheap hydroelectric power is therefore ideal. Later, oxygen was produced by evaporation of liquid air, which also requires cheap electricity to be economical. The economy of the Djeva arrangement can be judged from the fact that, when rubies were grown for research purposes in the author's laboratory in the late 1960's, the purchase price of a facetted stone from Djeva was lower than the cost of just the oxygen and hydrogen needed to grow a crystal of the same size in the laboratory. Apart from Eastern Europe and presumably China, Djeva now has a dominant position in commercial production outside Japan, where the Nakazumi company is the main supplier. Some 1400 furnaces were installed by Djeva in 1946 and the capacity of the factory is now 300,000,000 carats or 60,000 kg. Although the corundum crystals produced are used mainly to make bearing for watches and other instruments, Djeva rubies have also been used in lasers and their material was chosen for the Telstar satellite.

The manufacture of gemstones is now very much a sideline for Djeva, but the company has experimented with different **dopant** additives and has produced stones in an enormous range of colours. The current list of coloured corundums contains 32 different stones, although the last one is labelled 'No. 75', which indicates the very extensive range which has been produced at different times. Table 2.1 lists the manufacturer's number and name for the materials available at 4¢ to 9¢ a carat in the United States for boules or part

Fig. 2.5 (c) One of the furnace rooms at Monthey.

boules. It should be mentioned that these names are illegal in some
countries, because it is considered that they might be confused with
natural stones if they are applied in the facetted stones.

Table 2.1. Colour range of Djeva synthetic corundum

Number	Name
1	Ruby Topaz light rose
1A	Ruby Topaz rose
1 *dark*	Ruby Topaz rose
1¼	Ruby Topaz rose
1 *bis*	Ruby Topaz rose
2	Ruby Topaz dark rose
3	Ruby light rose
4	Ruby rose
5	Ruby dark rose
6	Ruby garnet colour (light garnet colour)
8 *sp.*	Ruby dark red or ruby dark garnet colour for jewellery
8	Ruby dark red
12	Sapphire white
20 *sp.*	Sapphire lemon yellow
21 *sp.*	Sapphire gold yellow
22 *sp.*	Sapphire orange yellow
25 *sp.*	Sapphire Topaz of Brazil
30	Sapphire bluish of India
31	Sapphire Ceylon light blue
32	Sapphire Ceylon dark blue
33	Sapphire Kashmir blue
34	Sapphire Burma blue
35	Sapphire Burma dark blue
44	Alexandrite light blue for big stones
45	Alexandrite
46	Alexandrite dark
47	Alexandrite greenish
50 *sp.*	Damburite
55 *sp.*	Padparadshah
61	Kunzite
65	Sapphire 'pourpre'
75	Corundum Djeva green

(Sp. = Homogeneous colour inside the boule)

An even greater range of coloured stones is available in synthetic spinel, which is also conveniently made by the flame fusion method. **Spinel** is the mineralogist's name for magnesium aluminate $MgAl_2O_4$, and the first synthesis of this material in the flame fusion furnace is credited to L. Paris, a student of Verneuil. Paris was studying the effect of various dopants on the colour of corundum. Magnesium, in combination with other elements, was found to cause major colour changes and it was eventually realised that these changes were produced by a change in the crystal structure of the material of the boule.

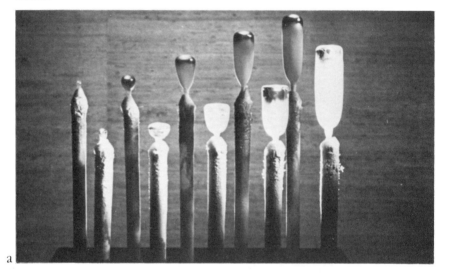

a

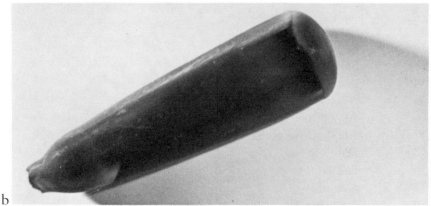

b

Fig. 2.6. (a) Sequence showing the growth of a ruby boule by the flame fusion method.
(b) A spinel boule.

A mixture of one part magnesium oxide MgO with one part alumina Al_2O_3 does not produce good quality boules, but the oxy-hydrogen furnace tends to produce a spinel which is deficient in magnesium. The best quality boules have a formula in which 5 parts Al_2O_3 are combined with two parts MgO. This difference between the composition of the synthetic spinel and that of the natural material means that synthetic spinel can be readily detected using measurements of physical properties such as density. Table 2.2 shows the list of coloured stones currently produced by Djeva.

Table 2.2. Colour range of Djeva synthetic spinels

Number	Name
100	white
101	bluish white
105	Aquamarine green
105 *bis*	Aquamarine bluish
105 *ter*	Aquamarine blue
106 *light*	Aquamarine light blue
106 *dark*	Aquamarine dark blue
108	Aquamarine bluish
108 *bis*	Aquamarine dark blue
109	Aquamarine bluish dark
111	Ceylon colour
112	Burma blue
114	Azurite light
115 *bis*	Azurite
116	Cyanithe
118	Aquamarine bluish (dark colour)
119	Aquamarine dark blue
120	Zircon blue
122	Zircon green
130	greenish yellow (Chrysolithe)
135	Brazil emerald green (Erinite)
136	Brazil emerald dark green
140	rose
149	green Tourmaline light green
152	green Tourmaline colour dark

The use of synthetic spinels and corundums to simulate the properties of totally different minerals such as alexandrite and

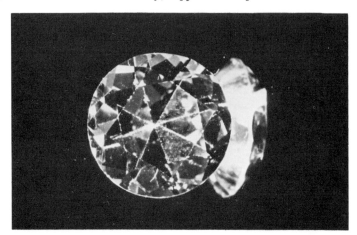

Fig. 2.7. Examples of corundum and spinel cut stones.

aquamarine raises the question of terminology. A synthetic spinel to simulate an aquamarine has to be considered an 'imitation', so rather than consider it primarily as an imitation aquamarine, it would perhaps be preferable to label the material 'pale blue spinel' and let it stand on its own attractiveness. This would conform to the requirements of the International Confederation of the jewellery trade (CIBJO).

Colourless spinels caused a furore in the mid-1930's, when they were marketed as a substitute for diamond – 'Jourado diamond'. Shrewd advertising and the scarcity of gem testing laboratories convinced sections of the public and of the jewellery trade that these stones could not be distinguished from diamond, and there was a brief panic as a collapse in the price of diamond was feared. Announcements were made over the radio by the Precious Stone section of the London Chamber of Commerce to assure the public that the 'Jourado diamonds' were not difficult to distinguish from diamond, and indeed spinel is a rather poor diamond substitute in comparison with the majority of stones discussed in Chapter 6.

STAR STONES

In 1947, the Linde Division of the Union Carbide Corporation in East Chicago began the production of star sapphire and ruby using the Verneuil process, and their method was patented [11] in 1949. Star-stones get their name from their appearance when viewed along the principal axis of the crystal. Six bright bands are seen radiating from the centre of the stone so that the bright feature resembles a simple representation of a star or asterisk (*). This **asterism** in corundum is caused by the presence of sets of tiny needles of aluminium titanate Al_2TiO_5, which are aligned in sheets at 60° to each other, matching the symmetry of the crystal structure. Asterism is produced by adding a small quantity of rutile, TiO_2, to the alumina powder. As the boule forms the rutile dissolves in the layer of molten alumina, but on cooling following solidification the titanium oxide separates out as needles not mainly of rutile but of Al_2TiO_5, which is formed by reaction of the rutile with the alumina. According to the Linde patent, the best results are produced by adding 0.1 to 0.3% of rutile to the powder used in the furnace and maintaining the temperature of the resulting boules at 1100–1500°C for several hours to crystallise out the Al_2TiO_5 needles. Star stones are normally prepared in the cabochon cut with rather steep sides, to display the asterism to best effect.

One of the main problems in preparing star stones is to distribute the Al_2TiO_5 needles uniformly so that the star occupies the whole width of the stone. The Linde crystal growers found that they obtained the best results by changing the oxygen flow rate so as to vary the temperature during growth in a periodic fashion. This was done most conveniently by intermittent closing of a valve to cut off part of the oxygen supply. The procedure was found to lead to a periodically-varying distribution of the needles, the lower flow rates causing them to be distributed across the whole width of the boule but higher rates giving a preferential distribution in the outer zone only. The star effect was most pronounced when the alternating layers were each 1 mm in thickness. This procedure illustrates one of the major advantages of man-made over natural gemstones: the crystal grower has control over the conditions under which the material is prepared and can vary these conditions to best effect. Although the advocates of natural gemstones accept certain treatments, such as the heating of zircons, as desirable to improve the appearance of these stones, they have no control over the conditions under which the natural crystals originally grew! Only rarely do natural star stones compare in sheer visual impact with their man-made counterparts.

Fig. 2.8. Linde star sapphire mounted in a ring.

Linde also produced **surface stars** by polishing rutile-free stones in the cabochon cut and then diffusing in rutile to form a thin layer of needles, prior to the final polish. These stones have a higher transparency than the normal star stones but have not been marketed on a wide scale.

Linde star stones have been produced in a range of colours, purple, green, pink, yellow and brown as well as shades of blue and red other than those of sapphire and ruby. Since the original patent has now expired there have been a number of alternative suppliers, for example in Germany, and a colourless star sapphire has been reported [12]. This competition has had the effect of lowering the price of synthetic star corundums, and Linde themselves have now ceased manufacture and sold their equipment, although the stones are still available from Elvin Co. of New Jersey. Djeva have probably now become the major supplier of star-stones, which are still very popular in the USA.

MISCELLANEOUS METHODS

In recent years there have been a number of scientific studies of the growth of corundum and spinel by the flame fusion method. These have mainly been concerned with the relation between defects in the crystals and the conditions used to grow the boule. The chief cause of imperfections in crystals grown by this method is the steep temperature gradient between the hotter region of the flame, where the molten tip of the growing boule is located, and the cooler region below. This sharp difference in temperature along the axis of the boule leads to a high degree of strain, and on removal from the furnace the boules often fracture to form two half-cylinders from which the stones are cut. The temperature gradient may be reduced by the addition to the furnace of an 'after-heater', either a small electric heater wound around the axis in the lower part of the flame, or alternatively a set of four small oxy-hydrogen burners mounted at right angles. Even with this precaution the crystals are more highly strained than those grown by other methods. The curved bands and gas bubbles which were noted by Verneuil in his original boules are still very frequently observed and enable the gemmologist to distinguish between natural stones and those grown by this flame fusion method (although the two types of stone are indistinguishable at a distance of a foot or so). Detailed studies of the flame fusion method, with drawings of the apparatus, have been published by Arthur Linz and colleagues at MIT [13] and S. K. Popov, who was mainly responsible for the growth of corundum crystals in the Soviet Union [14]. Studies at the Air Force Cambridge Laboratories were described in a review by Charles Sahagian [15]. He lists the colours produced by various elements in corundum; copper (golden), manganese (pink), vanadium (purple, but variable according to lighting), cobalt (grey-green), nickel (yellow), iron (grey), titanium (yellow), chromium + vanadium (blue to red), cobalt + vanadium (pale blue to red), cobalt + chromium (maroon), iron + titanium (blue-green). Similarly, the colouring effects of a few elements in spinel were also reported: chromium (pink, blue-red or deep red) cobalt + chromium (light blue), and manganese + vanadium (yellow-green).

Because flame fusion rubies are easily detected, there have been attempts at growing stones which more closely resemble the natural material, using alternative methods. Of these, that involving the use of a flux gives crystals which are most like the natural stones. Although flux-grown rubies had been produced in the 19th century, interest revived only when scientific laboratories began to investigate the application of high-quality ruby crystals as **masers** and **lasers**. This area of study began in the late 1950's and crystals of plate-like habit were grown by Eric White [8] at the GEC Hirst Research Laboratories, Wembley [16] and by Bob Linares [17] and Joe Remeika [18] at the Bell Laboratories, Murray Hill, New Jersey, using as a flux either lead fluoride or a mixture of this salt with lead oxide or boric oxide. The crystals were grown by cooling the solutions from about $1300°C$ to $900°C$ at $2°C$ per hour. In 1965, the GEC work had progressed to the stage where ruby crystals 4 cm $\times$ 4 cm $\times$ 1.2 cm had been grown, using a modified technique [19]. A seed crystal was suspended on wires in the middle of the solution, with small pieces of ruby held at the base of the solution to act as source material for the crystal growth.

This tendency of ruby crystals to grow from high temperature solution as plates rather than with all sides equal is a major problem for gem applications. The rate of lateral spread of the ruby plates can exceed the rate of thickening by as much as 100:1. This tendency appears to be stronger at lower temperatures, so that the goal of more equidimensional crystals, from which stones for facetting can be conveniently cut, can be more nearly gained by growing the crystals at temperatures above $1200°C$ or so. It has also been found

[20] that the incidence of plate-like crystals may be reduced by adding about 0.5% of lanthanum oxide to the solution. The lanthanum probably enters the crystals and may cause detectable changes in the optical properties. An alternative approach is to choose a flux in which the plate-like habit does not occur. Reports from the Soviet Union suggest that calcium tungstate and similar fluxes provide suitable high temperature solvents for the growth of non-platy crystals of ruby [21].

From the late 1950's onwards, the spate of research laboratory studies on the flux growth of rubies appeared certain to have some impact on the gemmological scene. It was about this time that Carroll F. Chatham of San Francisco, the pioneer of synthetic emerald production, started work on rubies, and during the last decade he has marketed flux-grown ruby. Photographs of his crystals show them to be equidimensional rather than plate-like, which suggests that the flux used is a tungstate or possibly a molybdate. The crystals are grown on light-coloured seeds of natural corundum and contain inclusion both in the seed itself and in the region of early growth around the seeds [22]. In 1969 the so-called 'Kashan rubies' made their appearance. These were produced in the United States by Ardon Associates and marketed by Designers Ltd. of Houston, Texas. The properties of these stones were reported in the journal *Gems and Gemmology* to be almost identical with those of the natural stones, except in their transparency to short-wave ultra-violet light and differences in their inclusions. Crystals grown from solution often contain particles of the mother liquid which have become trapped and solidified as the crystals were growing. The gemmologists speak of 'veils' and 'dot-and-dash' inclusions, and are normally able to distinguish flux-grown from natural rubies from the appearance of these. Indeed, they can also locate the place of origin of the natural stones from the same clues. The Kashan stones were produced only until 1972, but there have been a number of other suppliers in addition to Chatham.

Flux-grown ruby was also produced by Pierre Gilson, a report on these stones appearing in 1975 [23]. The rubies were grown on colourless seed crystals and exhibit the 'veil' inclusions which are not uncommon in flux-grown crystals. A lithium or lead molybdate flux was possibly used. Rubies not on the list of materials currently produced by the Gilson company and were not marketed on an extensive scale.

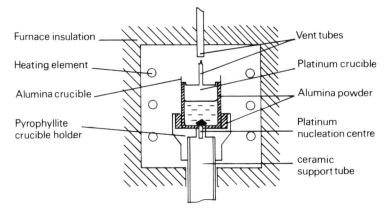

Fig. 2.9. Diagram of apparatus used for flux growth of oxide crystals in the author's laboratory.

Research on the flux growth of ruby still continues and an extensive study by Koichi Watanabe of Gunma University in Japan has provided interesting information on this method of crystal growth. Dr. Watanabe and his colleagues use cryolite (Na_3AlF_6) as flux and employ a gradient technique, with fused alumina maintained under a baffle at the bottom of the crucible and transported by convection, after it dissolves, to a seed crystal held in the melt above the baffle.

Since the 1960's rubies have been needed for lasers, which has led to the widespread growth of crystals by the method of pulling from the melt, first developed by J. Czochralski in 1918. In this method, the high temperature required to melt ruby is normally obtained from a radio-frequency induction heater. The power source feeds several kilowatts of electrical energy at a frequency of the order of 100 kilocycles per second into a water-cooled copper coil several inches in diameter and in length. As the current through the coil changes at high frequency, power is induced in any electrically conducting material placed near the coil. In the modern version of the Czochralski method, power is normally coupled into an iridium crucible containing the molten alumina *via* an outer crucible called a **susceptor** which is made from some cheaper material. The alumina is maintained at a temperature appreciably above its melting point and a seed crystal, cut in some chosen crystallographic direction, is introduced so that its lower end is just immersed below the melt surface. The upper end of the seed crystal, cooled by the conduction of heat through the seed holder, is at a temperature below the melting point and remains solid. The seed crystal is normally rotated in order to avoid variations in temperature around its circumference. Growth of the crystal is carried out by slowly raising it at a constant rate by the use of a motor which drives along a screw thread. The crystal grower must vary the temperature of the melt in such a way that the crystal diameter gradually increases from the seed diameter to that of the required crystal. With the largest apparatus now available, this could be four or even six inches. The diameter is then kept constant while the crystal is grown to the desired length. Control of the crystal diameter is now possible using various forms of automatic devices. These either weigh the crystal or crucible continuously during growth, 'sense' the emission of heat radiation from the curved liquid surface (meniscus) which surrounds the edge of the crystal, or utilise the reflection from this meniscus of light from a laser beam. The Czochralski method is not used only for ruby but is the established method of producing silicon crystals for the electronics industry. Silicon is the material from which transistors and integrated circuits are normally made.

Although Czochralski rubies have been facetted and may even have been marketed, they have not been commercially successful as gemstones, perhaps because they are more expensive to produce than flame-fusion grown rubies but can be fairly readily distinguished from the natural stones. The distinguishing features of the pulled crystals are **growth bands**, fluctuations in the intensity of the colour which are associated either with unstable convection in the melt or with the period of rotation of the crystal. Linde have patented the production of star stones by the Czochralski method, but the material sold has probably been produced by flame-fusion.

Rubies have also been grown by the hydrothermal process, in which the alumina and chromium oxide are dissolved not in a molten salt flux but in water at high temperatures and pressures. Rubies were prepared by this method in the late 1950's by Albert Ballman and Bob Laudise at the Bell Laboratories [25] and by Dick Puttbach, Roger Belt and Roch Monchamp at Airtron, New Jersey [26] using ruby seed crystals and adding sodium carbonate to the water solvent. Such additives are called **mineralisers**. Hydrothermal ruby has never been marketed as a gemstone, unlike hydrothermal emerald which will be discussed in the next Chapter.

Fig. 2.10. Flux-grown ruby with a natural ruby (not of gem quality) showing the similarity in crystal habit.

In spite of the modest popularity of flux-grown rubies, the corresponding flux-grown sapphires are almost unknown. These can be prepared by the same techniques used to grow ruby and it is difficult to explain their scarcity, although of course rubies are much more popular. However, a report in 1972 from the Gem Testing Laboratory in Hatton Garden complains of a skilful fake in which a 'crown' of natural green or yellow sapphire was joined by adhesive to a base of blue synthetic sapphire [27]. If this stone were mounted in a ring, it would be difficult to distinguish from a natural blue sapphire because examination with a lens would reveal the typical inclusions of natural sapphire (in the crown) and a spectroscope* would show the light absorption characterisitic of blue sapphire (in the base). Only if the stone is immersed in a liquid and examined from the side can the join be seen, and the deception revealed. Flux-grown sapphires have been produced by Koichi Watanabe using the method described above [24], by Chatham, and also by Deltronic Crystal Industries of Denville, New Jersey, who market flux-grown rubies as well.

Similarly, although flux-grown spinels have been prepared as high-quality crystals, there is little interest in these stones for gem

*See Chapter 9.

applications. The great majority of spinels grown were colourless and were produced for scientific studies. The only coloured flux-grown spinels known to the author were grown by Eric White and John Wood at Imperial College, London. Additions of nickel, cobalt, manganese, chromium and copper oxides to the spinel constituents results respectively in turquoise blue, deep blue, yellow, red and pale green crystals, all of pleasing appearance. The crystals were grown from solution in lead fluoride, by the relatively unusual technique of allowing the lead fluoride to evaporate over 6–7 days through a small hole in the crucible lid, with the temperature maintained at 1200°C [28]. Crystals up to 1 inch in diameter were produced. Commercial demand for flux-grown spinels is unlikely in view of the ready availability and low cost of stones prepared by flame-fusion.

Although of little interest in gemmology, an exciting new method has been applied to the growth of corundum which shows that it is possible to grow crystals of very complex shape at extremely rapid rates. In this **edge-defined**, **film-fed** (EFG) process, developed by Tyco [29], liquid alumina rises from a reservoir by capillary action, the tendency of liquids to rise through a small hole because of the force of attraction between the liquid and the material in which the hole is located. (This same force is responsible for the supply of water, and hence food, to growing plants.) The liquid alumina 'wets' the die through which the holes pass and the shape of the die can be highly complex. As the liquid contacts a seed crystal, which is then raised at a steady rate, the alumina solidifies into a shape which is determined by that of the die. In this way, single crystals of corundum have been prepared in very complex cross-sections such as a hollow rectangular tube with six or more circular holes. The rate of growth can be as high as 2 cm per minute or more, and it is astonishing to see long crystalline filaments being wound onto drums at a rate well above one metre per hour. This material has found several applications although, as might be expected, the quality of the corundum is not so high as in more conventional processes with lower rates of growth. As yet the EFG method has not been applied to gemmological areas, but it could be used to prepare ruby or sapphire in unusual shapes for *avant garde* jewellery.

REFERENCES

[1] R. Boyle, *An Essay about the Origins and Virtues of Gems*, 1672, reprinted by Hafner, New York, 1972.

[2]   P. M. E. Jannettaz, *Bull. Soc. Fr. mineralogie*, Paris, **9** (1886) 321.

[3]   R. Webster, *Gems*, Butterworth, London, 1970.

[4]   K. Nassau & R. Crowningshield, *Lapidary Journal,* **23** (1969) 114, 313 & 440.

[5]   M. A. Gaudin, *Comptes Rendus Acad. Sci.*, Paris, **69** (1869) 1342.

[6]   K. Nassau & J. Nassau, *Lapidary Journal,* **24** (1971) 1442, 1524.

[7]   A. Verneuil, *Comptes Rendus Acad. Sci.,* Paris, **135** (1902) 791.

[8]   A. Verneuil, *Ann. de Chim. et de Phys.*, **8** (1904) 20.

[9]   A. Verneuil, *Comptes Rendus Acad. Sci.*, Paris, **147** (1907) 1059.

[10]   A. Verneuil, U.S. Pats 988, 230 (March 28, 1911) and 1,004,505 (Sept. 26, 1911).

[11]   J. N. Burdick & J. W. Glenn Jr., U.S. Pat. 2,488,507 (Nov. 15, 1949).

[12]   R. T. Liddicoat, *Gems & Gemmology*, **14** (1974) 309.

[13]   A. Linz, E. F. Farrell, M. J. Berkebile and A. Vetrovs, M.I.T. Lab. for Insulation Research Report 185 (Dec. 1963).

[14]   S. K. Popov, *Growth of Crystals 2* (Ed. A. V. Shubnikov & N. N. Sheftal) Consultants Bureau NY 1959, p. 103.

[15]   C. S. Sahagian, *The Growth of Single Crystals* (1966) AFCRL – 66-33.

[16]   E. A. D. White, *Nature*, **191** (1961) 901.

[17]   R. C. Linares, *J. Applied Physics*, **33** (1962) 1747.

[18]   J. P. Remeika, U.S. Pat. 3,075,831 (Jan. 29, 1963).

[19]   E. A. D. White & J. W. Brightwell, *Chem. & Industry* (1965) 1662.

[20]   K. R. Janowski, A. B. Chase & E. J. Stofel, *Trans Am. Inst. Met. Eng.*, **233** (1965) 2087.

[21]   V. K. Yanovskii, I. V. Voronkova & V. A. Koptsik, *Soviet Phys. Crystallog*, **15** (1970) 302.

[22]   R. Crowningshield, *Gems & Gemmology*, **12** (1966/67) 110.

[23]   M. O'Donoghue, *J. Gemmology*, **14** (1975) 224.

[24]   K. Watanabe and Y. Sumiyoshi, *Journal of Crystal Growth*, **24/25** (1975) 666.

[25]   R. A. Laudise and A. A. Ballman, *J. American Chem. Soc.*, **80** (1958) 2655: A. A. Ballman, A. J. Caoraso & R. A. Laudise,

U.S. Pat. 2,979,413 (Apr. 11, 1961).

[26] R. C. Puttbach, R. F. Belt & R. Monchamp, ASD Project 8-132, AF Contract 33 (657) 10508, September 1964.

[27] B. W. Anderson, *J. Gemmology*, **13** (1972) 96.

[28] J. D. C. Wood and E. A. D. White, *J. Crystal Growth*, **314** (1968) 480.

[29] H. LaBelle Jr., *Mater. Res. Bull.*, **6** (1971) 581.

CHAPTER 3

Emerald

Emerald is without doubt the most attractive green gemstone. It is a member of the beryl family, like aquamarine and heliodor, which are silicates of beryllium and aluminium having a formula $Be_3Al_2Si_6O_{18}$. The green colour of emerald is due to the presence of chromium, probably replacing some aluminium in the above formula. This same **impurity** element gives ruby its characteristic redness. Natural emeralds also contain iron and vanadium, and the relative concentrations of these three main colouring elements determine whether the emerald is a pale green or some deeper shade ranging through to a deep bluish-green. Some beryls containing negligible concentrations of chromium may also be pale green, but purists argue that the colour of true emerald must be due to chromium. A typical emerald from Colombia, where the finest stones are mined, is found to contain 0.14% chromium, 0.12% iron and 0.05% vanadium. The most valuable stones should be a bright grass-green with a slight bluish rather than a yellowish tint. Good quality natural emeralds are extremely scarce, and the larger and more perfect stones can command prices around £10,000 per carat or more, often higher than the prices of the best ruby or diamond. Emeralds seen in high street jewellery stores often contain more inclusions than would be tolerated in other gemstones – just look at them carefully next time you pass a window, you don't need a lens to see the dark inclusions!

As mentioned in Chapter 1, the first successful synthesis of emerald crystals was reported by Hautefeuille and Perrey in 1888. They dissolved 18¾ g of the constituents of beryl with 0.6 g of chromic oxide in 92 g of lithium molybdate in a platinum crucible. They first melted the molybdate with the furnace at a dull red heat, then raised the temperature progressively over 24 hours to 800°C, which they maintained for 5 days. This procedure yielded about

15 g of small crystals. Later work, involving a heating period of 14 days, resulted in crystals 1 mm in diameter.

THE ESPIG PROCESS

These experiments were followed up in Germany at the IG Farben-Industrie, the crystals being sufficiently large for stones to be cut and marketed at 'igmeralds'. Although this work began in 1911, the technical details were not published until 1960 [1]. The main problem encountered both by Hautefeuille and Perrey and in the early studies at IG Farben was the large number of crystals which **nucleated** and grew in the crucible. If the process was to be commercially viable, it was necessary to find a way to control this nucleation process in order to grow a few large emerald crystals instead of many tiny ones. This problem was solved by H. Espig at IG Farben by the use of what is now called the **flux reaction technique** [2]. The technique differs from those in which crystals are grown by slow cooling of a solution, or by solvent evaporation, in that it involves a chemical reaction between the constituents of the crystal. In Espig's process, two of the major constituents of emerald, beryllium oxide BeO and aluminium oxide Al_2O_3, are dissolved in the lithium molybdate flux (solvent) but the third major constituent, silica SiO_2, floats on the surface of the solution. In order to make sure that the silica floats rather than sinks, the composition of the flux has to be carefully adjusted to give a relative density of near to 2.9, lighter than emerald but more dense than silica. Because emeralds themselves are relatively light, the additional precaution of placing a platinum screen above the emeralds in the solution in order to prevent them from floating up to grow among the silica is found necessary, since the crystals are then of very poor quality.

The process of formation of the emerald involves a chemical reaction between the silica and the beryllium oxide, the aluminium oxide and a little chromium oxide which is also dissolved in the molybdate flux. For this reaction to proceed, the silica must first dissolve in the flux and diffuse to a region where the concentration of all the reactants is sufficiently high for emerald to crystallise. The base of the crucible must be slightly cooler than the rest of the solution if the crystallization of emerald is to occur in this region. Once the first crystals have started to grow, nucleation of additional crystals in other regions of the crucible is not likely to occur provided that the silica arrives at a slow enough rate for it to be used up in the chemical reaction which produces the emerald. The success of this process therefore depends upon the very slow rate of migration of silica through the solution. As an alternative arrangement, the beryllium and aluminium oxides may be placed at the bottom of a crucible with the silica floating on the top of the solution as before. In this arrangement the emeralds grow in the intermediate zone, where seed crystals may be suspended.

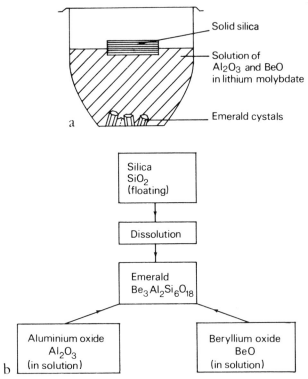

Fig. 3.1. (a) Arrangement used in Espig's method for the growth of emerald crystals.
(b) Diagram illustrating Espig's method.

The IG Farben process is very slow and emeralds require growth periods of up to a year. During this time the solution must be re-plenished with silica to make up for its rate of incorporation in the growing crystals. Crystals up to 2 cm in diameter have been grown, but these contained inclusion so that the stones cut from them were of about 1 carat in weight. Espig reported that chromium alone did not give the best emerald colour, but did not state whether he added vanadium and/or iron oxides to improve the colour.

Emerald production at IG Farben was discontinued in 1942 because of World War II. The same or a similar process was, however, used by the firm of Walter Zerfass of Idar Oberstein, Germany, and by Professor Richard Nacken in the Mineralogical Institute, Frankfurt. Controversy and confusion surround Nacken's work because he also grew quartz crystals by the hydrothermal method (as discussed in Chapter 6). In this method the solvent used to dissolve the emerald is not lithium molybdate or any other molten salt but simply water at high temperatures and pressures. The solubility of emerald in water at room temperature or even at its normal boiling point is very low, but increases very rapidly if the temperature is raised to 300 or 400°C. Of course water at such temperatures would boil extremely rapidly, and in the hydrothermal method it must be contained in a pressure vessel strong enough to withstand the very high pressure which it exerts, in the region of 1000 times atmospheric pressure. Emerald crystals grow in nature by the hydrothermal method, or more probably by a process which should be considered intermediate between the hydrothermal and flux methods since the solvent properties of the water will be modified by the presence of various mineral salts. Emerald in solution in such a liquid is present at high temperatures deep in the earth's crust. As this solution moves to less deep regions where the temperature and pressure are lower, the emerald tends to crystallize out, and crystals are particularly likely to be deposited in crevices provided that the deposition process can occur slowly over long periods. Evidence from the surface structure of natural crystals [3] suggests that they grow much more slowly than synthetic crystals. Becuase water is present in the medium from which natural crystals grow, they contain inclusions of water which can be detected by analytical instruments such as the infra-red spectrometer.

Kurt Nassau [4] has made a detailed study of Nacken's crystals and of the information available concerning their manufacture; he found no evidence that any of the crystals were grown by the hydrothermal method. Confusion can arise in cases where a layer of emerald is deposited on a seed crystal of natural, colourless beryl. The detectors will register the presence of water in the beryl crystal, and the investigator may conclude that the crystal is a hydrothermally-grown synthetic emerald if he fails to notice the central colourless region. Nassau speculates that Nacken may have been a consultant to IG Farben, and so may have been familiar with the floating silica process and even a contributor to its development.

MODERN COMMERCIAL MANUFACTURE

Current commercial production of emerald is dominated by two suppliers, Chatham and Gilson. Carroll C. Chatham, of San Francisco, began to experiment with the growth of emerald while he was still in college. His experiments continued as a part-time activity between 1930 and 1946, when full-time production began. Chatham has never patented his process, but it is not likely to be very different from that of IG Farben. Seeding is probably used infrequently, but some crystals have been grown to very large sizes: a crystal weighing 203 g (1014 carat) has been presented to the Smithsonian Institution in Washington, and one of 255 g (1275 carat) to Harvard University. The period of growth normally used is believed to be up to a year, as in the IG Farben production. However, this period could perhaps be substantially reduced if the crystals were grown in a stirred liquid rather than a stationary crucible and solution.

Chatham prefers to use the term 'cultured' rather than 'synthetic' to describe his emeralds, but this term was disallowed by a US Federal Trade Commission. Since 1963, the emeralds have been marketed under the name of 'Chatham created emerald'. The legal proceedings over the terminology gave the synthetic emeralds valuable publicity and helped to establish them with the jewellery trade. Chatham's work was honoured by the American Association for Crystal Growth who, in 1975, gave a special presentation at Stanford University in recognition of his pioneering work. Because of the delay in the publication of details of the IG Farben process, Chatham had only the Hautefeuille and Perrey papers to guide him during his early studies. It must also be remembered that he undertook his initial work in a period when flux growth was being used almost nowhere else in the world, and that Carroll Chatham was probably the first person to use flux growth of crystals on a commercial scale.

Many years have since passed and synthetic emeralds are now widely accepted and used even by the most conservative jewellers. The other major supplier is Pierre Gilson, formerly of Campagne-les-Wardecques, Calais, France and now based in St-Sulpice, Switzerland. Gilson entered the family brick company in 1935 after completing military service and taking an engineering degree at the Institut Catholique de Arts et Métiers in Lille. Interested in research from the start, in 1936 he created what was probably the only research laboratory in a small company in the whole of France. The laboratory introduced a number of innovations which led to new developments in industrial ceramics. When on a visit to the United States in 1950, Gilson was impressed with the achievements of Carroll Chatham, whose single-handed research had cornered the world market in synthetic emeralds.

Fig. 3.2. Pierre Gilson.

Pierre Gilson set out to discover the secrets of emerald synthesis for himself, and spent fourteen years in the development of a commercial process. According to literature provided by M. Gilson, he did not base his research study on the early work on emerald synthesis by Ebelmen and Hautefeuille and Perrey, but set out to find the solvent which would reproduce the best results achieved in nature. Chemical analysis of inclusions inside natural emeralds revealed a large number of possible contenders as constituents of the solvent used by nature to grow emeralds: boron, bismuth, lead, lithium, nickel, sodium, potassium, molybdenum, tungsten, vanadium, chromium, fluorine and oxygen in addition to water. In order to evaluate possible candidates for the 'geological soup', the first test was of the solubility of emerald, because high quality crystals cannot be grown from very dilute solutions except at low growth rates. The novel idea introduced as a further test consisted of observation of the

Fig. 3.4. Emerald seed plates being mounted on platinum holders prior to crystal growth.

solvent action on a crystal. A good solvent for emerald growth was considered to be one which would dissolve the crystal layer by layer rather than irregularly. The elimination of less promising materials at this stage was followed by trial experiments on the growth of emeralds under different conditions. The composition of the solvent finally chosen in 1964 is, of course, a closely guarded secret. However the analogy with nature is not one which has been pursued completely because natural emeralds contain inclusions which show that they grew from a partly aqueous 'soup' under high pressure, whereas Gilson emeralds are grown at atmospheric pressures from a water-free, molten salt bath.

The crucibles used by Gilson for emerald production are separated into two compartments, one used for crystal growth while the other contains the molten salt solvent which replaces that lost by evaporation during the long growth period. The raw material is said to be poor quality emerald from Madagascar and Brazil, so that the process is one of recrystallization rather than one involving a chemical reaction as in the IG Farben process. Seed crystals 4 cm $\times$ 1 mm are mounted on a noble metal frame and growth proceeds at a rate of 1 mm a month for nine months. The support wire can be seen in the final crystals and must be removed prior to cutting. Each crystal gives about 200 carats of emerald, and 500–1000 carats are obtained per run.

The emeralds sell for about $\frac{1}{10}$th of the price of natural ones, from $120–260 per carat for facetted stones. Synthetic emeralds are illegal in Colombia, where the world's finest natural emeralds are mined, and where there is a serious fear that man-made emeralds would be passed for natural stones. The value of the natural stones might then fall in view of the difficulty of distinguishing between synthetic stones and the most perfect natural emeralds.

Although Gilson's process, like Chatham's, is not known in any detail, a detailed study of various man-made emeralds [5] confirmed that Gilson, Chatham, Zerfass and Igmerald synthetics were all flux-grown. The most powerful evidence was the absence of water inclusions from all these crystals while all man-made hydrothermal emeralds, like the natural stones, contain about 1% water in the form of inclusions. The Chatham stones showed lithium impurities and it was concluded that a molybdate flux had been used to grow them, although only a trace of molybdenum showed up in the analysis.

HYDROTHERMAL EMERALD

Hydrothermal emerald has also been produced on a commercial basis, although never with great success. The first product to become widely known was that of Johann Lechleitner of Innsbruck, Austria, whose emeralds appeared around 1960 under the names of 'Emerita' and 'Symerald'. These stones were sold for a short time only, mainly because the layer of emerald deposited on the colourless beryl seeds was rather thin. Later a 'sandwich' was produced, with emerald coating a beryl seed and this emerald layer covered with a layer of colourless beryl. The green colour which is the main appeal of emerald was not well developed in either version, and the various layers could be readily detected by gemmologists, or even by eye if the stone was viewed from the side.

A superior stone was produced by the Linde Division of the Union Carbide Corporation of San Diego, California and the processes used are described in patents of 1971 and 1973 [6]. The introduction of chromium into the crystals was found to require the addition of an acid to the water solvent. Such additives, which affect the crystal growth conditions but which do not themselves enter the crystal, are known as **mineralisers**. Conditions used for growth of emerald were typically 500–600°C with pressures of about 700–1400 atmospheres.

As in the IG Farben method, the prevention of multiple nucleation of tiny crystals requires that the reactants be separated. The beryllium and aluminium oxides are located at the base of the liquid and the silica at the top, in a mesh container. Seed crystals are held on wires in the body of the solution and these grow at a rate of about 0.3 mm per day, much faster than in the flux method. The highest growth rate reported was 0.8 mm per day, recorded when the solution was made highly acid. The size of the crystals grown is limited by the size of the pressure vessel, because the source materials cannot be replenished without cooling the solution and releasing the pressure. The same seed may be replaced in a new solution up to three or four times. The more rapid growth rates achieved in the hydrothermal method are possible mainly because the seed plates are cut in such a way that the large area on which growth occurs is a crystallographic plane capable of much more rapid growth than the habit faces which eventually develop. Presumably the same procedure could be used to achieve faster growth rates in the flux method, although it must have been tried by Chatham and Gilson.

Production of Linde stones was terminated in 1970, possibly because of problems with cracks in the emeralds, but more probably because the company had adopted a policy of marketing their own 'Quintessa' jewellery rather than selling the stones to jewellers, and this practice was not really accepted by the established trade.

Hydrothermal emerald containing vanadium but no chromium has been produced by the Crystal Research Company of Melbourne, Australia [7]. The crystals were reported to weigh up to 10 carats, from which facetted stones of ½ to 2 carats were cut.

OTHER METHODS

There have also been a number of investigations into the growth of emerald by the flux method, mainly for application in masers in microwave communications rather than as gemstones. It has been found that a large number of fluxes may be used successfully [8]; lithium tungstate, $(Li_2W_2O_7)$, lead molybdate $(PbMoO_4)$, lead tungstate $(PbWO_4)$ or vanadium pentoxide (V_2O_5). Bob Linares and his co-workers at the Bell Laboratories in New Jersey noted that solutions of the emerald constituents in lithium molybdate formed a complex phase which appeared as red, hexagonal rods on cooling the solution. This phase tended to crystallize at temperatures below 650°C, while above 800°C the mineral phenakite (Be_2SiO_4) was crystallized. Although the beryl (emerald) phase is stable only up to 800°C in lithium molybdate, its stability range is increased to 1200°C in vanadium pentoxide. The rate of growth on a seed plate was as high as 1 mm per day. In Japan there has more recently been interest in the flux growth of emerald, leading to a number of patents [9]. Although emeralds of Japanese origin do not appear to have been

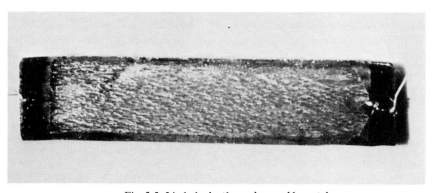

Fig. 3.5. Linde hydrothermal emerald crystal.

marketed, at least outside Japan, there may be a challenge to existing suppliers from this quarter.

In view of the difficulties met in growing emerald from solution, especially the slow growth rate, it would be attractive to be able to prepare emerald crystals from the melt. The difficulty here is not that emerald has a high melting point, but that it decomposes on melting (it is said to melt **incongruently**). In spite of this problem, Tony Gentile and his colleagues at the Hughes Research Laboratories have grown emerald by the Verneuil method using an oxy-hydrogen furnace [10]. A boule ½ inch in diameter and several inches in length was grown in 3–4 hours. This process seems very appealing, even though the boule did contain small gas bubbles. Although there have been speculations that the product may have been a glass, Dr. Gentile has confirmed that crystalline emerald was obtained. However, quality was not high enough to merit commercial development.

At present the existing suppliers of emerald appear to be capable of meeting world demand. Chatham and Gilson were joined in 1970 by Zerfass of Germany, and reports appear from time to time in the gemmological literature of small-scale experimenters apparently producing emeralds as a part-time interest, as Chatham and Gilson once did. The scarcity of good quality natural emerald may lead to an increased demand over the next few years, and possibly to an increase in the price of synthetic as well as of natural stones. The present world market, a few million dollars per annum, is rather small as yet for a really large chemical manufacturer to enter the emerald business.

Synthetic emerald is still one of the relatively few man-made gemstones which is accepted by the jewellery trade and which has its place alongside, but not really competing with, the natural material. Carroll Chatham has expressed to the author his view that, although his product was at first regarded with great hostility by the established gem business, it has had the beneficial effect of regulating the demand for natural emerald, and so has prevented stocks from being depleted almost to extinction.

Other synthetic beryls have been reported, with different colouring elements in place of chromium. Nickel produces a pale green stone, manganese a greyish-green, cobalt a pinkish-brown, copper a pale blue and iron a deep blue. These stones are produced in Australia and the Soviet Union, probably by the hydrothermal method. The pale blue variety of beryl, aquamarine, is the most popular after emerald and synthetic stones could attract a substantial market. At present, however, synthetic aquamarine and other coloured beryls apart from emerald are very rarely encountered. The recent discovery of a deep red beryl in the Wah Wah mountains of Utah provides another interesting gem material which may become very popular and which already appears to be established as a collectors' item. The red combines well with emerald and duplication of this stone in the laboratory is a new challenge for beryl crystal growers.

REFERENCES

[1] H. Espig, *Chemical Technology,* **12** (1960) 327.
[2] D. Elwell & H. J. Scheel, *Crystal Growth from high temperature Solutions,* Academic Press, London, 1975.
[3] I. Sunagawa, *American Mineralogist,* **49** (1964) 785.
[4] K. Nassau, *J Crystal Growth,* **35,** (1976) 211.
[5] E. M. Flanigen, D. W. Breck, N. R. Numbach & A. M. Taylor, *American Mineralogist,* **52** (1967) 744.
[6] E. M. Flanigan, US Patent 3, 567, 642, (March 2, 1971); E. M. Flanigen & N. R. Mumbach, US Patent 3, 567, 643 (March 27, 1971); P. J. Yancey, US Patent 3, 723, 337 (March 27, 1973).
[7] A. M. Taylor, *J. Gemmology,* **10** (1967) 211.
[8] R. C. Linares, A. A. Ballman & L. G. van Uitert, J. Applied Physics 33 (1962) 3209.
[9] M. Ushoi & Y. Sumiyoshi, *Nippon Kagaku Kaishi* (1972) p. 1648.
[10] A. Gentile, D. M. Cripe & F. H. Andres, *American Mineralogist,* **48** (1963) 940.

CHAPTER 4

Diamond

The most popular of all gemstones is the diamond. It has been so for centuries, particularly since the development of the brilliant cut, a form of facetting which shows the optical properties to best effect. Its fire and brilliance are high, but the diamond's outstanding property is its hardness and durability. Hardness is normally measured on the **Mohs** scale, which is formulated in terms of the material's resistance to scratching. The order of hardness is given on a scale from 1 to 10, with ten standard materials being chosen to provide a simple criterion of 'scratchability'. The standard materials, in order of hardness, are: (1) Talc, (2) Gypsum, (3) Calcite, (4) Fluorspar, (5) Apatite, (6) Feldspar, (7) Quartz, (8) Topaz, (9) Corundum, (10) Diamond. As an example, a stone which can be scratched by quartz but not by feldspar is given a hardness of 6½. Glass, which is normally considered to be a hard material, has a hardness of only 5 but a copper coin has a hardness as low as 3. Glass can therefore be scratched easily by quartz, so the ability to scratch a window is a poor test for diamond! The Mohs scale rather underestimates the distinction of diamonds, for on the alternative **Knoop** scale diamond is more than five times harder than sapphire (hardness 9), but sapphire is only 30% harder than topaz (hardness 8) on this scale. It has been said that diamond is to steel as steel is to butter.

The great hardness and handsome appearance of diamond are difficult to reconcile with the fact that diamond is one form of carbon, the other form being graphite. Amazingly, graphite and diamond are chemically identical, but diamond is the hardest natural material known while graphite is used in pencils and will draw a line on a sheet of ground glass. An even more remarkable comparison is between diamond and amorphus (non-crystalline) forms of carbon-charcoal, coke and soot! The enormous differences in properties between graphite and diamond result from differences in the arrangement of carbon atoms in the two materials. Diamond has a cubic crystal structure with each carbon atom surrounded by four identical atoms, forming a regular tetrahedal pyramid. The very strong chemical bonds between adjacent carbon atoms are therefore distributed symmetrically and the great hardness of diamond results from the inherent stability of this regular array. In contrast, graphite has a layered structure with the very strong bonds between carbon atoms only effective within the layer, where the atoms form a hexagonal arrangement. The bonds between layers are very weak, so that adjacent layers can slide easily past each other, and this explains the lubricant properties of graphite.

As early as the 17th century, Robert Boyle showed that diamond was affected by a flame, and G. Averani and C. A. Targiono of the Florence Academy in Italy demonstrated in 1694 by the use of a burning glass that diamond will burn if heated to a high enough temperature. In 1772 Antoine Lavoiser showed that carbon dioxide is produced when carbon is burned, but the proof that diamond is a form of carbon is credited to the English chemist Smithson Tennant. The crucial experiment was performed in 1797, when Tennant burned a diamond in a closed gold vessel and showed that the weight of carbon dioxide produced was exactly that expected if a diamond consists of carbon only. An identical weight of carbon dioxide gas would have been obtained by burning the same mass of graphite or soot in place of the diamond.

Following this discovery came a gradual realisation that diamond is the form of carbon which is stable at high pressures. To convert inexpensive graphite into nature's hardest and most glamorous material, we need to squeeze the atoms closer together. There is still controversy about the origin of diamond in nature, for the high pressures and temperatures now known to be required for diamond to be the stable form are reached only at a depth of over 100 km (60 miles) below the earth's surface. Some scientists are reluctant to accept that diamonds could have survived a journey from such great depths, and have advanced theories of formation in shallower regions. The most likely explanation is that the diamonds did form deep in the earth's mantle, probably in molten peridotite, a rock containing oxides of iron and magnesium but low in aluminium, silicon, sodium and potassium compared with the earth's crust generally. Conditions for the growth of diamond must have remained stable over long periods, until the build-up of pressure of carbon dioxide gas caused the ejection of the diamonds to some shallower depth. In most cases, the diamonds did not reach the surface immediately but remained at a high temperature where partial dissolution and migration of nitrogen into the crystals took place. Finally a second unstable condition is envisaged, with very rapid ejection to a region near the earth's surface. There the diamonds either remained or were carried away by the effects of wind and rain to be distributed in an **alluvial** deposit, perhaps very far from the point of emergence.

The diamonds not found in alluvial deposits are located in **pipes** of the rock kimberlite, a bluish material which is clearly not a lava because diamonds would burn if subject to the temperature of lava in the absence of a high pressure. The composition of kimberlite is not that of the original diamond-bearing liquid, as changes have taken place since the upwards flow and solidification of this liquid over 100 million years ago. Kimberlite pipes, mainly found in South Africa, are not uncommon and the high price of diamond was maintained, until the recent scarcity, only by careful control over mining and marketing.

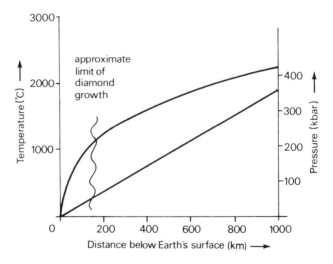

Fig. 4.1. Approximate variation of temperature and pressure with distance below the earth's surface.

EARLY ATTEMPTS AT SYNTHESIS

'*La production du diamant est un probleme pour les chimistes moderne le pendant de la pierre philosophe pour les alchimistes*' (H. Le Chatelier 1908).

Although the attempts to synthesise ruby in the 19th and early 20th centuries can confidently be said to have been successful, it was diamond that attracted the attention of a multitude of experimenters. The very earliest attempts were extremely optimistic, for they preceded the knowledge of its composition. The first serious experiment may have been one by the Russian V. Karazin in 1823. J. W. Mellor's standard textbook on inorganic chemistry [1], in which the above quotation appeared, mentions 29 experimenters who claimed to have made diamonds in the period between 1828 and 1924. The earliest of these attempts, by the French scientist C. Cagniard de la Tour in 1828, is still remembered although it was later shown that the 'diamonds' were alumina or silica. However the majority of the early experiments, for example E. de Boismenu's electrolysis of molten calcium carbide or G. Rousseau's decomposition of acetylene at 3000° using an electric current, are now largely forgotten even by writers who review diamond synthesis. On the other hand, few experiments have attracted considerable publicity, mainly because they were for many years believed to have been successful. The earliest such series was that of J. B. Hannay.

James Bannantyne Hannay was born in 1855 at Cove Castle, Helensburgh, Scotland, which remained the residence of his family. He did not like school and left at fourteen to help his father at Glasgow's Grand Theatre, which his father owned. James developed an interest in chemistry early in life, first to help him make fireworks but also because of the need for coloured fires then used in producing special effects in the theatre. He borrowed books on the subject and set up a laboratory at home then, four years after leaving school, started work at Shawfield Chemical Works in Glasgow. In 1873, at the tender age of 18, he published six papers on chemical analysis and in 1876 he became works manager. At only 21 he was elected a Fellow of the Royal Society of Edinburgh and left industry for college. He was strongly influenced by Sir William Ramsay who was his senior by two years and his close friend. His most important scientific papers were dated from 1877 and in 1878 he was appointed Assistant Lecturer at Owens College, Manchester, but remained only a few months because of ill health. From this time on he set up his own laboratory to concentrate on industrial problems. The synthesis of diamond became his major study and his results were published in a paper to the Royal Society in 1880 [2]. The basic idea was that organic compounds such as paraffin would decompose when heated with an alkali metal such as lithium, the hydrogen in the paraffin combining with the lithium and so liberating carbon. The carbon was expected to dissolve in the vapour under high pressure, and to crystallize as diamond. The experiments were performed by heating a mixture of about 90% hydrocarbon, a few milligrams or grams of lithium and 10% 'bone oil' (a mixture of nitrogen-containing compounds made by distillation of bones, for which Hannay was seeking commercial uses) in sealed tubes of wrought iron. The tubes were 20 inches long, ½ inch bore and eventually of 1½ inch thick walls. The open end was sealed by a blacksmith's weld, and the presence of volatile liquids inside made it not surprising that, 'It requires great skill on the part of the workman, and it is only one man in a hundred who can perform the operation with invariable success'. The tubes were heated to redness and maintained at this temperature for several hours, and in only three out of a series of 80 experiments did the tube survive without leaking or exploding. In his paper to the Royal Society in 1880, Hannay commented on the strain of the experiments: 'The continued strain on the nerves, watching the temperature of the furnace, and in the state of tension in the case of an explosion, induces a nervous strain which is extremely weakening, and when the explosion occurs it sometimes shakes one so severely that sickness supervenes'. The danger of the experiments was also made apparent in the same paper: 'A list of disasters now awaited me. Eight tubes failed through bursting and leaking and one of the explosions, when two were heated together, destroyed a part of the furnace and injured one of my workmen'.

The 'successful' experiments yielded a few tiny crystals, which were described as very hard, containing 98% carbon and having a relative density of 3.5. It is clear that Hannay believed that he had produced diamond, and his experiments were reported in the *Times* by M. H. N. Story-Maskelyne, Keeper of Minerals at the British Museum. However, the scientific community became increasingly sceptical about Hannay's claims. He turned to writing books on religion and philosophy, and is said to have eventually developed eccentric tendencies and died in a mental home.

In 1939 Prof. M. W. Travers of University College, London

wrote an article [3] on Hannay's work, stressing his experimental talent and many scientific achievements. Strong interest was revived in 1943 when F. A. Bannister and Kathleen Lansdale [4] found an exhibit labelled 'Hannay's diamonds' in the mineralogical collection of the British Museum and subjected them to X-ray diffraction analysis. All but one of the twelve crystals was found to be diamond. This discovery stimulated a series of letters to the journal *Nature*, by Travers [5], C. H. Desch [6] and Lord Rayleigh [7]. Rayleigh recollected that his father, who had been one of the secretaries of the Royal Society in 1885–96, had frequently spoken about Hannay's experiments and had mentioned that he had sent papers to the Society on diamond production after 1880, but that these had been rejected. I asked the Royal Society whether such papers were, in fact, in their files but the archivist found only a rejected paper of 1893 on the metallurgy of lead. It is presumably this paper that Lord Rayleigh's father had recalled.

The chances that Hannay did produce diamonds are extremely remote. The pressures which were generated in his tubes could not have been higher than about 2000 atmospheres*, at least ten times lower than that required for diamond to be the stable phase of carbon. Later attempts to repeat his experiments with improved engineering and methods of diamond detection were all unsuccessful. It seems clear that the diamonds tested by Bannister and Lonsdale were natural diamonds substituted for the real products of the experiments. This was recently confirmed in a study of the Hannay diamonds by electroluminescence [8]. There have been a number of testimonials to the effect that Hannay himself was above deception, but the true story behind 'Hannay's diamonds' is likely to remain a mystery. The intriguing twist in the tail of the Hannay story is that the diamonds tested by Bannister and Lonsdale were of a rare and pure 'type II', and the chances that the faker would select by chance this rare type to make the 'switch' seem remote! Whatever the truth, Hannay must be credited with the first systematic experiments to use high pressures for diamond synthesis and his hunch that diamonds would crystallise from solution was an inspired one which later experimenters would have been well advised to note.

Some ten years after Hannay's experiments, Prof. Henri Moissan in France introduced a very different technique based on rapid

*One atmosphere (the pressure due to the Earth's atmosphere) is about 14 lb on each square inch; 2,000 atmospheres is therefore just over 10 tons per square inch.

cooling of a solution of carbon in molten metal. This method was suggested to him by the discovery of small diamonds in the Canyon Diablo meteorite. Moissan was an innovator in the use of the electric arc furnace[†], which he used to melt iron with sugar charcoal, and his experiments are described in a book called *Le Four Electrique* [9]. At 3000°C the white-hot crucible was plunged into cold water, the idea being that a tremendous pressure would be generated as the solidifying outer shell of the melt contracted onto the inner core. After the crucible had been cooled to room temperature, the iron was dissolved in acids and the residue then treated with potassium hydrogen fluoride to remove all minerals except diamond. The experiments did give a number of tiny crystals, some of which had the optical properties of diamond and gave carbon dioxide on burning in oxygen. Bismuth, lead or silver in place of iron gave similar results. Moissan's claim was not universally believed but, unlike Hannay's, was accepted by Mellor [1]. As in the Hannay method, the pressures which Moissan could achieve are now known to be much lower than those required for diamond production, partly because the cast iron could not stand really high pressures but mainly because of a misunderstanding of the effect of rapid cooling of a molten metal.

The identification techniques available in Moissan's time were extremely unreliable, especially with crystals as minute as these. The most frequently used test was to place them in a silica boat and heat them in a stream of oxygen, watching for a flash of light if any of the crystals burned. The flashes which Moissan saw could have been due to minute particles of soot, coal or other dust which were present even when a boat seemed to be clean [10]. None of Moissan's products remains, not even photographs which could be studied by modern methods. It has been reported [11] that Moissan's widow believed her husband had also been a victim of fraud by one of his assistants, who had placed diamond fragments into the residues to 'please the old man and to avoid the tedium of long digestions'.

Around the turn of the century, Sir William Crookes [12] exploded cordite in closed steel tubes and calculated that his pressures reached 8,000 atmospheres. He had calculated that carbon would liquefy if heated to a sufficient temperature and would crystallize as diamond if the pressure exceeded 2350 atmospheres. Crookes was an

†Moissan was awarded the 1906 Nobel prize in chemistry for his work on the electric furnace and for the isolation of the element fluorine.

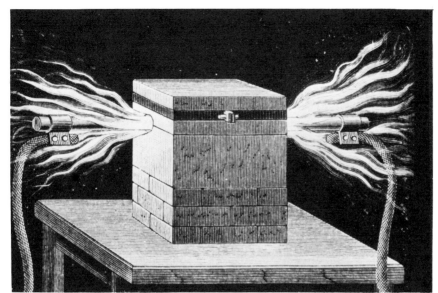

a

b

Fig. 4.2. (a) Moissan's 'Electric Furnace' with high temperature discharge.
(b) Moissan's method of quenching a melt of carbon dissolved in iron by plunging
into water.

authoriative supporter of Moissan's claim and gave a demonstration of the latter's method to the Royal Institution in 1897 [13].

Moissan's and Hannay's experiments were repeated by several investigators. In 1917 a German, Otto Ruff [14], reported success with Moissan's method, but he later changed his opinion and stated that he believed that his supposed diamonds were not genuine. The most celebrated and extensive study of the early methods was that of Sir Charles Parsons, shipbuilder and inventor of the steam turbine. From 1887 diamond synthesis became Parsons' hobby, one on which he spent hundreds of thousands of pounds. He had the advantages of his own engineering skills and the large hydraulic presses of his shipbuilding works, which could generate static pressures of 10,000 atmospheres. In a review of his work [15] presented to the Royal Society as the Bakerian lecture of 1918, Parsons reported that even a pressure of 15,000 atmospheres was not high enough to crystallize carbon. Although at that time he accepted Moissan's claim, Parsons confirmed that Moissan's method did not generate very high pressures, and that impurities such as silicon, aluminium and chromium greatly increased the crystal residue, while very pure iron gave practically no residue. Moissan's 'diamonds' were found to be probably spinels, and later repetitions by M. Seal and A. R. Bobrowsky gave crystals which proved to be silicon carbide, alumina or some unidentified amorphous material.

Parsons tried all the known methods and introduced some new ones, notably by firing high-velocity rifle bullets into cavities containing the materials to be compressed. The first of these used a 'Duck gun of 0.9 inch bore' which fired a steel piston into a barrel containing acetylene and oxygen. The gun was loaded with '2 drachms of black sporting powder, which amount had been calculated from some preliminary trials'. The compression was 288 to 1, and Parsons calculated that the resulting explosion would give him 15,000 atmospheres and 15,250°C, although the latter figure is very optimistic. Still higher pressures were expected by firing a 0.303 rifle into a small graphite charge: Parsons calculated from the deformation of the block into which the bullet was fired that his pressures momentarily reached about 300,000 atmospheres. These experiments produced only 'a few very minute crystals resembling diamond', showing that pressure alone could not be responsible for the formation of diamond because this is 'one quarter to one half that obtaining at the centre of the Earth'. Parsons believed that successful diamond synthesis required the presence of iron, although he had discouraging results when Moissan's experiments were repeated with a pressure at least three times as high as Moissan could have achieved.

Although Parsons believed at the time of the Bakerian lecture that he had achieved the synthesis of small diamonds, this view was later retracted. In 1928 Parsons and his assistant H. M. Duncan placed all their observations in the hands of C. H. Desch, and his letter to *Nature* [10] summarising the results reports that, 'the

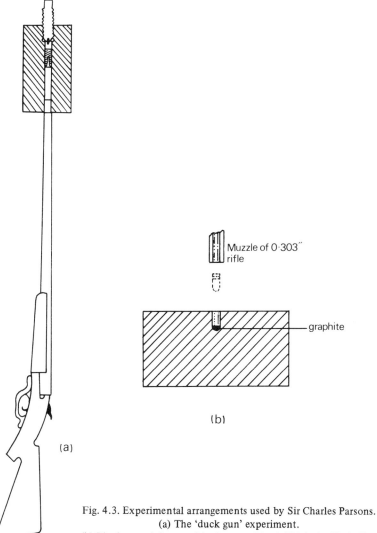

Fig. 4.3. Experimental arrangements used by Sir Charles Parsons.
(a) The 'duck gun' experiment.
(b) Block containing graphite impacted by 0.303 inch rifle bullet.

conclusion seems inevitable that diamonds have not yet been produced in the laboratory, and that investigators have been misled into regarding as diamonds various transparent, singly-refracting minerals which happen to be very resistant to chemical reagents'.

During the 1930's, Prof. J. W. Hershey of McPherson College, Kansas used to give Moissan's experiment as a project for his senior chemistry class, and claimed a record 'diamond' of 2 X 1.5 X 1 mm. Apparently there may still be militant local sentiment in McPherson, Kan. to the effect that the synthesis of diamonds is an old story [11].

Another approach to the diamond problem is based on the idea that molten graphite would crystallize as diamond on cooling. As we have seen, this was originally the idea of Sir William Crookes [12]. However it may have been adopted because of the feeling that, since graphite is very difficult to melt, solving this problem might somehow solve the similarly difficult problem of diamond synthesis. Attempts along these lines were made by James Basset in France and John M. Morehead of Union Carbide in the USA.

In 1933 Hans Karabacek obtained a German patent for a complex process of diamond synthesis involving heating and cooling cycles applied to carbon monoxide or carbon dioxide under pressure. He also acquired a large collection of minerals which was later bought by Harvard University. The collection was displayed in the Harvard museum and included a case labelled 'Karabacek's synthetic diamonds', apparently made using his patent. When these were eventually examined, however, the impurities in the diamonds were found to show all the characteristics of diamonds mined in South Africa! [11].

THE FIRST SUCCESS

The development of the high pressure apparatus necessary for diamond synthesis owed much to the pioneer of high pressure studies and Nobel prizewinner, Prof. P. W. Bridgman of Harvard University. Bridgman regarded the synthesis of diamond as a challenge to his inventiveness and technical ingenuity, and is said to have attempted it each time he began experiments with a new technique which led to an increase in the maximum pressure attainable. Bridgman was not only an eminent scientist and inventor but an entertaining writer as well. On diamond synthesis he wrote [11], 'The attempts to solve this glittering problem have revealed the whole human spectrum: those engaged in it have ranged from first-rate scientists to downright muckers and charlatans'. He reported that, over 25 years, an average of two or three people a year had offered to share their secret and the profit of making diamonds in return for his constructing the apparatus to put the idea into practice. He also once reported with characteristic humour that. 'The problem has got into the thriller literature, and I have often encountered the belief that the successful solver of this problem would be in danger of his life from the Diamond Syndicate'.

Bridgman, like Parsons, soon found that the transformation of graphite to diamond was difficult to achieve by pressure alone. Theory indicated that diamond should be the stable crystalline form of carbon above about 20,000 atmospheres, but Bridgman discovered that pressures of 425,000 atmospheres at room temperature and 70,000 atmospheres at red heat did not cause graphite to transform. Similarly, diamond at one atmosphere pressure is just as stable. Until she changed it for a much larger garnet, my wife went around confident in the knowledge that the diamond in her engagement ring would not one day turn into graphite, even though graphite is more stable than diamond at everyday temperatures and pressures. Diamond is said to be **metastable** at low pressure, and similarly graphite may remain in an unchanged, metastable form even under conditions where diamond is the stable phase.

The transformation of diamond to graphite can be achieved by heating to about 1500°C and it was suspected that the attainment of a similar temperature at high pressure was necessary for the reverse transformation. Bridgman began a project for high temperature synthesis in 1941 with financial support from the Norton Co. and General Electric Carboloy Division. At first the graphite was heated to 3000°C prior to transfer to the working chamber of a 1000 ton press. Then a chemical reaction involving **thermite** was used inside the chamber to achieve 3000°C for a few seconds simultaneously with pressures of 30,000 atmospheres. After four years diamonds had still not been produced, and the apparatus was moved to the Norton Company plant where it was used for continued experiments and for other work.

Eventually the Research Laboratory of General Electric took up the problem, and in 1955 came the first report of success by the team of Francis Bundy, Tracy Hall, Herbert Strong and Robert Wentorf. Although a group in Sweden later claimed to have synthesised diamond in 1953, their work was not published and so the GE group were able to obtain world patents. Their success was the result of a study lasting four years. The announcement of diamond synthesis increased the share value of GE by over 300 million dollars in a day and the stock of the De Beers mining syndicate fell by a few points, but recovered the next day. At the time of the announcement the diamonds which had been produced were extremely small, and it was said that a good sneeze at the wrong time could have led to the loss of the whole world supply!

The man who is credited with the first confirmed synthesis of diamond is H. Tracy Hall, whose personal account of this event has appeared in review articles in three journals [16–18]. Hall joined the GE Laboratory in 1948 and in 1951 became a member of a small group working on diamond formation, 'Project Superpressure'. Although a chemist by training, he decided that the major barrier to diamond synthesis was the lack of high-pressure equipment and designed a system later called the **Half-belt**. This was only moderately successful but pointed the way to the now famous **belt** design. However Hall could get his improvised version built only by an unofficial arrangement with friends in the machine shop. A similar subterfuge was needed to have the critical components re-made in tungsten carbide, after which pressures of 120,000 atmospheres (nearly 2 million pounds per square inch) could be achieved with temperatures of $1800°C$, lasting for several minutes. Experiments were pursued unsuccessfully for about a year, then on December 16, 1954 came the first success [17]. Hall later wrote, 'My hands began to tremble; my heart beat rapidly; my knees weakened and no longer gave support. My eyes had caught the flashing light from dozens of tiny triangular faces of octahedral crystals . . . and I knew that diamonds had finally been made by man'. This experiment had been performed at 70,000 atmospheres and $1600°C$ using graphite together with troilite (FeS). The diamonds were stuck to a tantalum disc used to carry the current for heating the sample and this may have reduced the FeS to iron because sulphur alone will not cause the transformation to diamond.

The synthesis of diamond was confirmed on December 31st 1954 by Hugh Woodbury and this confirmation led to the press release of February 15, 1955. It was this clear confirmation by an independent investigator that was lacking in the Swedish (ASEA) claim.

The apparatus for diamond synthesis introduced by Hall is termed

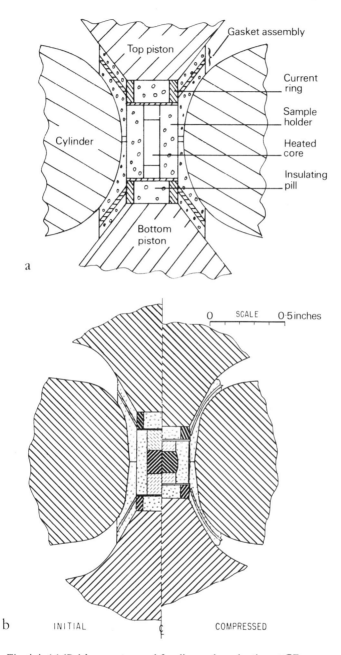

Fig. 4.4. (a) 'Belt' apparatus used for diamond production at GE.
(b) Illustrates the changes in dimensions which occur when the system is pressurised
to the extent used for diamond growth.

the 'belt' because the central zone in which the diamonds are made is supported by a ring made of tungsten carbide with pre-shrunk high-strength steel [19]. Two tapered pistons are driven by a large hydraulic press of strengthened steel. The great problem in the design of apparatus to produce high pressures and high temperatures is that steels and other structural materials rapidly lose their strength on heating. This problem can be solved only by internal heating of the working volume, with thermal insulation to prevent excessive heating of the pistons and belt. The General Electric group made good use of a naturally occurring rock, pyrophyllite, which becomes soft enough to transmit pressure but remains below its melting point at the high pressures used. The space enclosed by the pistons and belt is filled with a complex array of pyrophyllite and metal gaskets, and with a cylindrical carbon tube through which an electric current is passed to achieve the required temperature. The pyrophyllite acts as a gasket to seal any gaps, and provides thermal insulation when the sample is heated.

The critical factor missing in unsuccessful experiments such as those of Parsons and Bridgman was the **catalyst**, for example iron. It is now known that this material provides a solvent in which the graphite first dissolves, then recrystallises as diamond. Without the metal solvent, the rate of transformation of graphite to diamond is so slow as to be negligible even though the temperature and pressure are sufficient for diamond to be the stable form. According to the original GE patent [20], a typical composition of the reaction zone was 5 parts graphite to 1 part iron, $\frac{1}{3}$ part manganese and $\frac{1}{3}$ vanadium pentoxide. This mixture was sealed and heated to 1700°C under a pressure of 95,000 atmospheres for two minutes, then cooled to 1500°C in 8 minutes. There have since been a number of studies of potential solvents, especially by Wentorf [21], and the solvent which is most commonly used now is a mixture of nickel and iron. The nickel-iron alloys permit transformation to occur under less severe conditions, for example 50,000 atmospheres (still about 350 tons on each square inch) and 1400°C. It has also been shown that graphite can be replaced as the source of carbon by a wide variety of organic materials, wood, coal, tar, pitch or even peanut butter!

Although the General Electric diamond initially cost more than that dug out of the ground, they were able to achieve competitive prices for grit used in grinding wheels as early as 1957. A GE press release of October 22, 1957 announced that 100,000 carats of industrial diamond had been produced to date, that the current price was $4.25 per carat, and that 3½ million carats were expected to be produced during 1958.

The details of the GE synthesis were kept secret for many years, but the process has now been described in a series of papers [22, 23]. Tracy Hall became disenchanted both with the government-imposed secrecy and with the frustrations of company politics and funding and moved in September 1955 to Brigham Young University, where he now holds the prestigious post of Distinguished Professor of Chemistry.

The Swedish work which parallelled that at GE was carried out by the Allmana Avenska Elektriska Aktiebolaget, known as ASEA. Their study of diamond synthesis began in 1942, but details were published only in 1960 [24]. Apparently the ASEA group failed to report details of their success in synthesising diamond in 1953 because they were seeking to produce gem material, and were not aware of the importance even of very small diamonds for industrial applications.

The ASEA process involved pressures of 80,000 to 90,000 atmospheres and temperatures as high as 2760°C. In order to concentrate the pressure into a small region, six four-sided pyramids were mounted in the form of a cube with their points coming together and enclosing a spherical chamber about 400 cubic cm. in volume. Three pairs of hydraulically driven pistons were used to apply pressure to each of the pyramids, the whole piston assembly being mounted in a tube 52 cm in diameter and 78 cm high, strengthened with steel bands. Heating was initially by ignition of thermite, a mixture of magnesium metal with barium peroxide which produces very high temperatures when reacting chemically. Insulation around the thermite was provided by a 5 mm layer of soapstone inside a copper holder, and the core region inside the thermite contained the reactants, graphite and iron carbide inside a tantalum sphere. The high temperature produced by the thermite persisted only for a few minutes before falling due to heat conduction through the relatively massive pistons. It is a characteristic feature of both the GE and ASEA processes that only two to three minutes are required for the production of small diamonds used for cutting, grinding and polishing in industry. All the diamonds produced by the two processes are much less than 1 mm in diameter and a typical run at ASEA yielded

20–50 diamonds some 0.1–0.5 mm in size. ASEA later used electrical heating, with currents up to 1500 amps, and obtained a higher yield of diamonds.

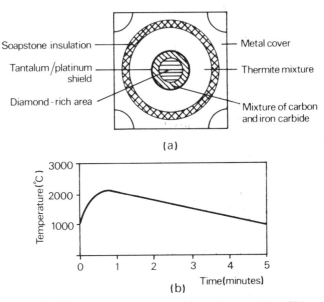

Fig. 4.5. (a) Arrangement of working volume used by ASEA.
(b) Plot of temperature versus time after ignition of the thermite charge.

The very successful GE 'belt' high pressure apparatus has been partly superseded by a tetrahedral-ram design [25], developed by Tracy Hall at about the same time. This design offers the advantage of very high pressures achieved with relatively cheap presses. Initially four independent presses were used, mounted in a symmetrical frame and converging on a central working space. An alternative and even simpler modification requires only a single hydraulic press, with the force in the other three directions being obtained by the reactions of the anvils on the conical surface of a strong steel support. In the latest version of the tetrahedral anvil apparatus, a spherical working surface is machined in the central region and contains tungsten carbide inserts which are relatively hard and strong in comparison with the steel of the anvils. A tetrahedral space is provided between these inserts and this contains machined pyrophyllite pieces, with space for a carbon cylinder which is heated by an electric current conducted through two of the anvils or in separate leads. The graphite sample and metal solvent are inserted into this cylinder.

Fig. 4.6. Tetrahedral ram apparatus developed by Tracy Hall.

Diamonds are now produced in several countries and over half of industrial diamond is now synthesised, at a price competitive with that of mined diamond. Among the leading producers is the South African mining corporation of De Beers, which decided within a month of the 1955 announcement by General Electric that it too would begin to manufacture the synthetic material. The De Beers factory at Springs near Johannesburg began production in 1958 and now has 75 high pressure units. A subsidiary was opened at Shannon in the Irish Republic in 1963, and in 1967 De Beers and ASEA (who did not begin commercial manufacture until 1964) agreed to combine production. Industrial diamond is now produced in China, Czechoslovakia and the Netherlands, by Komatsu in Japan and extensively in the Soviet Union. The world consumption of industrial diamond is more than 100 million carats (20 tons) per year, and some hundreds of tons of graphite must now have been converted into diamond.

GEM DIAMOND

The fabrication of diamond on this immense scale does not mean that it is a simple matter to produce diamonds of gem size and quality. The small volume which can be maintained under the extreme conditions required for diamond formation is a handicap in attempts to obtain large crystals, and in addition large crystals inevitably require long growth periods. The growth of gem diamond was not patented until 1967, when Robert Wentorf succeeded in growing diamond on a seed crystal [26]. The seed crystal is essential if crystallisation of graphite is to be prevented, even though the conditions are chosen to be within the region where diamond is stable. The main problem in growing large crystals is to operate in the diamond-stable region while maintaining a low rate of diamond deposition, so that the crystals grown are of good quality. In the technique used, the seed crystal was mounted in the cooler region of a solution at a temperature of about 1420°C, while small diamond crystals were placed in the lower region at about 1450°C. Pressures used were in the range from 55,000 to 60,000 atmospheres. It was found advantageous to locate the seed crystal in the lower region, since any tiny crystals formed away from the seed tended to float to the hotter region and re-dissolve, rather than growing around the seed.

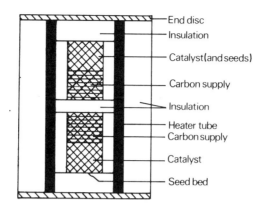

- End disc
- Insulation
- Catalyst (and seeds)
- Carbon supply
- Insulation
- Heater tube
- Carbon supply
- Catalyst
- Seed bed

Fig. 4.7. Arrangement used for the growth of large diamonds using transport of carbon in a metal solution under pressure.

In some of Wentorf's experiments, the diamond feed material was recrystallised as graphite. Such experiments have to be considered very expensive failures! However, a more serious problem was that the maximum rate at which the crystals could grow without instability was found to decrease as the crystals got larger. For a crystal of 1 mm in diameter, the most rapid rate of stable growth was found to be $\frac{1}{5}$ mm per hour. When the crystal size reached 5 mm, stable growth could proceed only at $\frac{1}{25}$ mm/hr, so that it took several days to grow a crystal of this size. This problem would be more serious if larger diamonds were to be attempted. To date, the largest synthetic diamond grown is about 6 mm in diameter and weighs 1 carat (0.2 g). Because of the rather slow growth rate, and the cost of maintaining a high temperature and pressure, the larger synthetic diamonds are appreciably more costly to produce than natural stones of comparable size. This cost difference can be removed only by the development of new apparatus which permits high pressures and temperatures to be maintained more economically than is possible with present technology. However, Robert Wentorf's large diamonds do represent a spectacular achievement as an example of crystal growth under difficult conditions. These synthetic diamonds are the purest diamonds in the world. A few have been cut and polished, and examples have been presented to the Smithsonian Institution in Washington and to the former GE research director William D. Coolidge (inventor of the X-ray tube) on his 100th birthday.

Fig. 4.8. 1-carat synthetic diamond grown by Robert Wentorf of GE, together with the graphite used as the starting material.

Coloured diamonds may be grown by **doping** the crystals with different elements. Nitrogen produces a green colour, and is probably responsible for yellow stones if it is present in a low concentration. Boron results in blue diamonds, as in the rare natural blue stones, the most famous being the Hope diamond which is a very deep blue. Studies of the properties of doped diamonds have been valuable in understanding some of the secrets of diamonds and their method of formation in nature.

DIRECT TRANSFORMATION OF GRAPHITE TO DIAMOND

The direct transformation of graphite to diamond requires even more extreme conditions than when a metal solvent is used. This is because of the great stability of graphite, due to the very strong bonds between its atoms. The first experiments to achieve a direct graphite-to-diamond transformation were reported in 1961 by P. S. DeCarli and J. C. Jamieson of the Allied Chemical Corporation [27]. A high-explosive charge was used to generate a pressure in the region of 300,000 atmospheres (about 2,000 tons per square inch) lasting for about a millionth of a second (one microsecond) with a temperature estimated as roughly 1200°C. This pressure was applied to a graphite sample and the presence of some diamond was confirmed in it, but the particles were very small. These crystallites, about 100 Å (10 nanometers or a hundred-thousandth of a mm) are comparable in size with 'carbonado' found in meteorites, which is thought to be formed during the intense shock wave as the meteorite strikes the earth's surface.

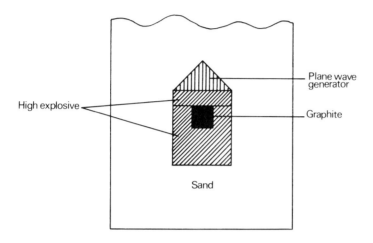

Fig. 4.9. Arrangement used by DeCarli and Jameson for the growth of diamonds using high explosive.

In 1963 Francis Bundy of General Electric succeeded in directly transporting graphite to diamond under steady pressures exceeding 130,000 atmospheres [28]. These pressures were obtained using a modified form of the belt-type apparatus, with larger piston faces and reduced length of the working volume between the pistons. Improved strengthening of the apparatus was necessary to withstand the higher pressures. The experiments involved flash-heating of bars of graphite to temperatures above 2000°C. Heating was by a pulse of electricity, and temperatures necessary for the formation of diamond persisted for some milliseconds (thousandths of a second), considerably longer than in the DeCarli and Jamieson experiments. The particle size was some two to five times larger than that produced by shock compression. Both sets of experiments were of value in constructing the **phase diagram** of diamonds, the graph showing the regions of pressure and temperature over which diamond, graphite and liquid are stable.

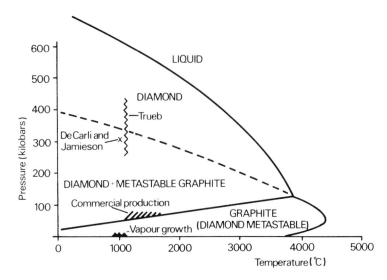

Fig. 4.10. 'Phase diagram' of carbon showing stability ranges of different phases and the conditions used in some of the experiments described in this Chapter.

Interesting experiments were performed by Bundy with J. S. Kasper [29], who used single crystals of graphite in place of the polycrystalline material of previous experiments. The diamond crystals produced in their first experiments had the normal cubic crystal structure. DeCarli and Jamieson had noticed, however, that the transformation to diamond occurred more readily when graphite particles in their samples were aligned along the so-called **c-axis** normal to the hexagonal sheets. When Bundy and Kasper mounted a single crystal so that pressure could be applied parallel to the c-axis, and the electrical resistance of the crystal was measured as pressure was applied, an increase in this resistance was noted when 140,000 atmospheres was reached. This increase was thought to be associated with the transition to diamond, although release of the pressure resulted in reversion to graphite. However, when this procedure was accompanied by heating of the sample to 900°C or above, crystallites of a new high pressure phase were formed, having a hexagonal structure rather than the normal cubic. Hexagonal carbon is also found occasionally in nature, especially in meteorites, and has been given the name **lonsdaleite** in honour of the late Dame Kathleen Lonsdale of University College London, whose major contributions to crystallography included studies of diamond.

In 1968 patents were granted to G. R. Cowan, B. W. Dunnington and A. H. Holtzman of DuPont de Nemours & Co. for a new process of shock-compressing metal blocks, for example of cast iron, containing small inclusions of graphite [30]. The pressures generated are above the 1 million atmosphere level and the metal, being less compressible than the graphite, serves the function of cooling the inclusions very rapidly. This stops the diamond formed during the pressure wave from reverting back to graphite after the passage of this wave, a tendency observed during the cold compaction experiments on single crystals. The material formed by this DuPont process is partly hexagonal carbon, so confirming that lonsdaleite tends to form under conditions of very high pressure and relatively low temperature. Material prepared by this **shock-quench** process is sold commercially for polishing purposes.

Further studies involving modifications of one or other of these processes are reported from time to time. L. C. Trueb [31] extended the DeCarli-Jamieson method to produce 250,000–450,000 atmosphere pressures of 10–30 microsecond duration, with a post-shock temperature reaching 1100°C. The graphite used was in the form of platelets 0.5-5 μm (thousandths of a mm) in diameter, and the diamonds produced were of similar size. However these particles were found to be made up of aggregates of much smaller cubic diamonds, in the size range 10–40 Å and 100–1600 Å. At present the Allied Chemical material does not appear to have been marketed, and it seems that this process still requires further development before it can compete with the solution or DuPont methods. The potential advantage of a shock-compression process is that an explosive is an inexpensive way of producing high pressures.

GROWTH UNDER METASTABLE CONDITIONS

Attention has been given in recent years to the attractive proposition of preparing diamond under conditions where graphite is the stable phase and diamond is therefore metastable (which means that it will survive indefinitely without transforming back to graphite). In order to transform graphite into diamond the carbon atoms must be excited to a high energy, normally by the application of high temperatures and pressures. The alternatives considered here are based on the principle that if carbon atoms can be produced in a very energetic state, on condensation to a solid form they may **pause** at the metastable diamond state rather than the stable graphite form. The 'pause' may be promoted by the use of diamond seed crystals, which encourage the carbon atoms to condense in the diamond arrangement rather than that of graphite.

The most promising approach is probably that based on the decomposition of a carbon-containing gas at fairly low gas pressures. The gas is decomposed as it flows over small diamonds, so releasing carbon atoms at the surface of the diamonds. This process was developed independently in the early 1960's by W. G. Eversole of Linde in the USA [32] and by B. V. Derjaguin and B. V. Spitsyn at the Institute of Physical Chemistry in Moscow [33]. Initially Derjaguin and his colleagues used carbon tetraiodide CI_4, while Eversole used methane CH_4, which has remained the most popular gas for this method. It was some time before the scientific community accepted that diamond really can be deposited by this method, but the evidence in favour of the validity of the process is now overwhelming.

Eversole's growth conditions involved a temperature between 600°C and 1600°C and a total pressure of one atmosphere, but with the methane concentration between 0.015% and 7% of the gas mixture. The diamond seeds were only 0.1 μm (a ten-thousandth of a mm) in diameter, to provide a large surface area for deposition. Unfortunately diamond is not deposited alone, because graphite clusters tend to form in the vapour and some of these are deposited with the diamond on the crystal surface. If the graphite is not removed by intermittently halting the process, it reaches a concentration high enough to interfere with the deposition of diamond. In Eversole's process the diamonds are periodically withdrawn and transferred for a few hours to a pressure vessel containing hydrogen at 1000°C and 50 to 200 atmospheres. The hydrogen reacts more rapidly with the graphite than the diamond so that graphite is removed and the diamond surface cleaned for further growth.

Derjaguin's group has found it advantageous to oxidise the graphite deposit using the oxygen in air at atmospheric pressure. This has the advantage that deposition and graphite removal may take place in the same reactor, with air introduced at intervals for the oxidation stage. Typical conditions now used for the growth of diamond are a temperature of 1020°C and a methane pressure of 0.07 torr (about 0.001% of an atmosphere). The fastest growth rates claimed are in the region of 0.1 μm (a ten-thousandth of a mm) per hour, with one carat deposited per hour in the whole reactor. Vibration of the seeds to surround each particle with methane leads to an improvement in the material grown. Even faster growth rates are possible by irradiating the diamond surface with light from a high-tensity xenon gas-discharge tube. The radiation is delivered in pulses, to cause the diamond to grow rapidly but not allowing many graphite crystallites to nucleate. Growth rates of several μm per hour are said to have been achieved under such pulse conditions. Occasionally the pulse method results in the formation of diamond 'whiskers', tiny filaments which project from a few spots on the surface, but the reason for these strange growths is not known.

In the United States, Eversole's work has been continued mainly by J. C. Angus and his colleagues at the Case Western Reserve University, Ohio [34]. Their growth conditions of 1000°C and 0.2 torr pressure of methane (mixed with hydrogen) are similar to those of the Soviet group, and the increase in weight is typically 6% in 20 hours, correspondingly only to 0.001 μm per day linear growth rate. Much higher growth rates are observed during the initial stage, probably because of the strain which occurs because the distance between the carbon atoms is slightly different in the film and in the crystal below. Presumably the very rapid growth rates quoted by the Soviet group also refer to this initial stage.

In the earlier experiments, diamonds treated by this vapour process were said to acquire a light gray colour. A more recent paper [35] contained the interesting comment, from a gemmological viewpoint, that off-white diamonds subjected to a series of deposition and cleaning cycles undergo a change in colour to light blue. The stage has not yet been reached when large diamonds can be prepared by deposition from vapour onto a seed crystal, and there is also no evidence that diamond layers can be deposited uniformly over the surface of relatively large stones. It is possible, however, that refinement of the method may allow facetted diamonds to be enhanced by the deposition of high quality material, possibly with some dopant such as boron to produce new colour effects.

An alternative technique, which has the merit of using elemental carbon rather than its compounds, involves the acceleration of carbon ions to high energies in the electric field [36]. Positive ions of carbon are produced in an electrical discharge at low gas pressures and these are accelerated and then guided by a magnetic field through a narrow opening into a deposition chamber at extremely low pressure. Here the carbon ions arrive with very high velocities (equivalent to a temperature of tens of thousands of degrees) and strike either a diamond seed crystal or perhaps a metal needle to be used in a record player. It has still not been confirmed that the surface coatings produced are of diamond, and the material deposited is probably amorphous.

In addition to the experimental techniques described above, there have been a number of alternatives proposed and patented. These are described briefly in collections of gem patents and in References [37, 38].

DIAMOND IRRADIATION

A chapter on diamond would not be complete without reference to the use of nuclear radiation to produce coloured diamonds. This treatment has been developed because of the scarcity of naturally-occurring coloured diamonds, and a good quality coloured diamond may be counted more than 25% more valuable than its colourless counterpart. A recent controversy in Switzerland which made international news concerned a stone whose value was put at either £60,000 or £600,000, according to whether or not it had been given radiation treatment.

The Victorian scientist and spiritualist Sir William Crookes discovered that exposure to radium turns diamond green. This change was later found to be due to α-particle bombardment, which causes colouration only of the outer layer of the diamond because the α's have low penetrating power in solids. The green colour, which is not very attractive, may be eliminated by re-polishing the stone to remove the coloured layer, or by heating the diamond to 450°C.

Irradiation of diamonds was largely forgotten until the emergence of nuclear physics in the late 1940's. A cyclotron was then used to accelerate deuterons (nuclei of heavy hydrogen -deuterium, which consists of a proton bound to a neutron) and to use these particles to bombard diamond. The diamonds became strongly radioactive for a few hours, but the net result was again a coloured outer layer. Bombardment by high energy electrons was found to produce a pale blue or green colour, again only in a thin layer. However, neutrons have a much stronger penetrating power and are able to produce a colour change throughout the body of the stone. The resulting stones are green, but heating these green stones at 900°C in an inert gas

. 2.11. Selection from the author's collection showing the range of coloured spinels and corundums.

Fig. 3.3. Gilson emeralds.

causes a change to brown and then to golden-yellow. These latter colours are more attractive than the green, and brown and yellow irradiated diamonds are quite popular in the United States.

A minority of diamonds show a very different response to irradiation, and occasionally blue, red and purple stones may be produced. These different colours depend on impurities present in the diamonds. The majority of diamonds, now designated type I, contain nitrogen as an impurity, presumably introduced into the stone at the intermediate stage between formation and ejection from the hotter regions below the earth's surface. In most of the diamonds the nitrogen is distributed in tiny platelets, but one in a thousand has it dispersed uniformly throughout the material. The latter are designated type Ib, while the majority are called Ia. Type II diamonds, which are less common, are purer and contain almost no nitrogen. The larger stones, such as the Cullinan, are of this type. Again a subdivision is necessary into type IIa, which form the majority, and the very rare type IIb containing a small concentration of aluminium impurity (hexagonal 'diamonds' are called type III). It is the unusual types Ib and IIb which can be coloured red or purple, and these stones are therefore more valuable than the less common types. A summary of the colour effects produced by irradiation on a commercial basis is given in Table 4.1 [39]. In general only the larger stones are considered suitable for irradiation, because the increase in value of smaller stones does not justify the cost of the treatment.

Table 4.1

Colour changes on irradiation

Type:	Ia	Ib	IIa	IIb
Treatment				
Neutron irradiation	Green	Green	Green	Green
Neutron irradiation + heating	Yellow-amber		Brown	Red-purple
Electron irradiation	Green	Blue or greenish-blue	Blue or greenish-blue	
Electron irradiation + heating	Yellow-amber	Red-purple	Brown	

While irradiation to produce colour changes is now an accepted technique in gem treatment, there are problems for the gem testing laboratories in distinguishing irradiated stones from those which have been coloured by the evaporation of a thin layer of some coloured material.

Irradiation is also used to produce colour changes in other gemstones. Examples of the use of irradiation to produce coloured varieties of quartz are quoted in Chapter 6, and there has been controversy and some confusion concerning a type of irradiated blue beryl called Maxixe beryl [40]. As is so often the case when the properties of gemstones are changed by some treatment, the problem which has faced gemmologists is that of distinguishing the Maxixe beryl from natural gemstones of a similar colour.

One problem with irradiated stones has been investigated by Nancy King of the *National Enquirer*. This is that some diamonds may retain a long-term radioactivity, due to the presence of impurities with long-lived isotopes. The extent of this problem is unknown but, in view of the danger to the wearer, owners of irradiated stones are advised to check for residual radioactivity.

REFERENCES

[1] J. W. Mellor, *Comprehensive Treatise on Inorganic and Theoretical Chemistry*, Vol. V, Longmans Green, London, 1924.

[2] J. B. Hannay, *Proceedings of the Royal Society,* **30** (1880) 450.

[3] M. W. Travers, *Chemistry and Industry,* **17** (1939) 507.

[4] F. A. Bannister & K. Lonsdale, *Nature,* **151** (1943) 334.

[5] M. W. Travers, *Nature,* **152** (1943) 726.

[6] C. H. Desch, *Nature,* **152** (1943) 148.

[7] Rayleigh, *Nature,* **152** (1943) 597.

[8] A. T. Collins, *Industrial Diamond Review* (1975) p. 434.

[9] H. Moissan, *Le Four Electrique* (The Electric Furnace) English translation by Arnold, London, 1904.

[10] C. H. Desch, *Nature,* **121** (1928) 799.

[11] P. W. Bridgman, *Scientific American,* November 1955, p. 42.

[12] W. Crookes, *Diamonds,* London, 1909.

[13] W. Crookes, *Diamonds,* reported in Annual Report of the Smithsonian Institution, 1896/97, p. 219.

[14] O. Ruff, *Zeitschrift fur Anorganische Chemie,* **99** (1917) 73.

[15] C. A. Parsons, *Philosophical Transactions of the Royal Society,* **A220** (1920) 67.

[16] H. T. Hall, *Proc. 3rd Biennial Conference on Carbon,* 1957, p. 75.

[17] H. T. Hall, *Jnl. of Chemical Education,* **38** (1961) 484.

[18] H. T. Hall, *The Chemist*, **47** (1970) 276.
[19] H. T. Hall, *Review of Scientific Instruments*, **31** (1960) 125.
[20] H. T. Hall, H. M. Strong & R. H. Wentorf Jr., U.S. Patent 2,947 610 (Aug. 10, 1960).
[21] R. H. Wentorf Jr., *Bericht. Bunsenges. Phys. Chem.*, **70** (1966) 975.
[22] H. P. Bovenkirk, F. P. Bundy, H. T. Hall, H. M. Strong & R. H. Wentorf Jr., *Nature* 184 (1959) 1094; F. P. Brundy H. M. Strong & R. H. Wentorf Jr., *Chemistry & Physics of Carbon*, **10** (1973) 213.
[23] A. M. Beuche, *Proc. Royal Institution* (GB), **47** (1974) 287.
[24] H. Liander & E. Lundblad, *Arkiv. Kemi*, **16** (1960) 139.
[25] H. T. Hall, *Review of Scientific Instruments*, **29** (1958) 267.
[26] R. H. Wentorf Jr., U.S. Patent 3,297,407 (Jan. 10, 1967); Jnl. of Physical Chemistry 75 (1971) 1833.
[27] P. S. DeCarli & J. C. Jamieson, *Science*, **133** (1961) 182.
[28] F. P. Bundy, *Jnl. of Chemical Physics*, **38** (1963) 631.
[29] F. P. Bundy & J. S. Kasper, *Jnl. of Chemical Physics*, **46** (1967) 3437.
[30] G. R. Cowan, B. W. Dunnington & A. H. Holtzmann, U.S. Patent 3,401,019 (Sept. 10, 1968).
[31] L. C. Trueb, *Jnl. of Applied Physics*, **42** (1971) 503.
[32] W. G. Eversole, U.S. Patents 3,030,187 & 188 (April 17, 1962).
[33] B. V. Derjaguin & D. B. Fedoseev, *Scientific American*, **233** (1975) 102.
[34] J. C. Angus, H. A. Will & W. S. Stanko, *Jnl. of Applied Physics*, **39** (1968) 2915.
[35] D. J. Poferl, N. C. Gardner & J. C. Angus, *Jnl. of Applied Physics*, **44** (1973) 1428.
[36] S. Aisenberg & R. Chabot, *Jnl. of Applied Physics*, **42** (1971) 2953.
[37] D. MacInnes, *Synthetic Gem and Allied Crystal Manufacture*, Noyes Data Corp., 1971.
[38] M. J. O'Donoghue, *Synthetic Gem Materials*, Goldsmiths Company, 1976.
[39] See B. W. Anderson, *Gemstones for Everyman*, Faber, London, 1976.
[40] K. Nassau, B. E. Prescott & D. L. Wood, *American Mineralogist*, **61** (1976) 100.

CHAPTER 5

Diamond Substitutes

PROPERTIES OF COLOURLESS GEMS

Perhaps 'Colourless Man-Made Gemstones' would be a better title for this Chapter. However, since diamond is accepted as the supreme colourless gemstone, it is the standard against which others are judged. Before the advent of synthetic stones, the most popular alternatives to diamond were zircon and colourless sapphire. Sapphire has the advantage of being close to diamond in hardness, but its brilliance and fire are much lower and it is very easy to see that the stones are not really comparable. Zircon does have a fire close to that of diamond but its brilliance is much lower, and only a little above that of sapphire.

The brilliance of a stone mainly depends upon the refractive index, which measures the degree to which a light wave is slowed down as it enters the material. The higher the refractive index, the slower the speed of light in the material compared with that in air. The refractive index also measures the amount by which light is bent as it enters the material, and it follows that materials of higher refractive index will exhibit a higher brilliance. The more the light is bent as it enters the material, the lower the angle it makes with the back surface of the stone, and the higher the probability that it will be reflected from this back surface rather than passing through. The amount of light reflected from a stone also depends on the angle of incidence of the light and on the cut of the stone, but it is the difference between the refractive index of diamond (2.42) and sapphire (1.77) which makes diamonds sparkle while colourless sapphires are relatively dull.

Many minerals exhibit **double refraction**, which arises because of the interaction of light waves with the regularly arranged atoms in

those crystals which do not have cubic symmetry. In doubly refracting crystals, the refracted light is broken up into two rays which
travel at different speeds and so are generally refracted at different
angles. This splitting means that the material has two refractive
indices, one for each of the two refracted rays. These are termed the
ordinary and **extraordinary** light rays, and they vibrate at right angles
to each other. The difference between the two refractive indices is
called the **birefringence**, which can be positive or negative according
to whether the refractive index for the extraordinary ray is greater
or less than that for the ordinary ray.

It is preferable for colourless gemstones to have zero birefringence,
that is for them to be optically isotropic (or members of the cubic
crystal system which display the same properties in all directions).
Diamond is isotropic, and so does not suffer from the major defect
of doubly refracting gemstones. When seen through the crystal their
facet edges have a fuzzy appearance because the eye sees two images
of the back surface.

The 'fire' of a gemstone is measured by its **dispersion**, which is
the difference in refractive index of the stone for different wavelengths of light. Standard wavelengths of 6870 Å (red) and 4308 Å
(violet) are chosen for the determination of the two refractive
indices. Because light of any colour is refracted at a different angle
from light of some other colour, this leads to the 'rainbow' colours
seen in light reflected from gemstones.

Table 5.1 shows the hardness, refractive index (for yellow light),
dispersion and birefringence of natural and synthetic stones which
are used as diamond simulants. In the case of doubly refracting
materials, the refractive index quoted is that of the ordinary ray,
and the birefringence is the difference in refractive index at the same
wavelength for the extraordinary ray.

Spinel was the first synthetic alternative to diamond when it was
produced in the Verneuil furnace. Its fire is a little higher than that
of sapphire but its hardness and refractive index are lower and it is
generally considered only marginally preferable as an inexpensive
alternative to diamond. In spite of this, its original introduction as
'Jourado diamond' caused a minor panic in the jewellery trade, as
mentioned in Chapter 2. Spinel is still sold as one of the cheapest
diamond substitutes. An advertisement of February 1978 offered
a complete 'gold-filled' ring with 1 carat spinel for $4.95 and one
with a 2 carat stone for $7.95.

5.1 Table of Properties of some diamond simulants

Material	Hardness	Refractive Index	Birefringence	Dispersion
Diamond	10	2.42	0	.044
Corundum	9	1.76	.008	.018
YAG	8–8½	1.833	0	.026
YAlO₃	8–8½	1.938	.017	.039
Spinel	8	1.72	0	.020
Cubic zirconia	7½–8½	2.15–2.18	0	.060
Yttria	7½–8	1.92	0	.050
Zircon	7½	1.92	.059	.039
GGG	6½–7	2.02	0	.038
Rutile	6–7	2.60	.287	.280
Lithium tantalate	5½–6	2.22	0	.087*
Strontium titanate	5–6	2.41	0	.190
Lithium niobate	5½	2.30	.09	.120

*Based on data supplied by F. A. Halden of Crystal Technology Inc.

RUTILE

The first post-war synthetic gemstone was rutile, which was originally produced as a by-product of research aimed at new whiteners for paint. Single crystals were required for research aimed at a better understanding of titania pigments, for example measurements of wettability and optical properties. Rutile is the stable oxide of titanium TiO_2, and occurs in nature only as an unattractive dark brown or black stone, usually with a high concentration of iron. The first synthetic rutile to appear on the jewellery market was made by National Lead Industries [1] in the United States, and was promoted in 1948. The outstanding property of rutile is its dispersion, which at 0.28 is more than six times that of diamond. This 'fire' is the highest of all gemstones, and gives cut rutile stones an astonishing appearance, with a very exciting play of colours. The refractive index is also higher than that of diamond, but the stones suffer from the disadvantage of a high birefringence which gives a marked 'fuzziness' to the rear facet edges. Rutile has a hardness below 7 and is therefore not very durable in the facetted form which best shows its unusual optical properties. In spite of this disadvantage, its remarkable appearance has made rutile very popular especially during the 1950's. Although it was most commonly marketed as 'Titania', many other trade names were used and a list of these gives some impression both of its popularity and of its unique properties [2] : Astryl, Brilliante, Diamothyst, Gava Gem, Jarra Gem, Johannes Gem, Kenya Gem, Kima Gem, Kimberlite Gem, Lusterlite, Miridis, Rainbow Diamond, Rainbow Gem, Rainbow Magic Diamond, Sapphirized Titania,

Star-Tania, Tania-59, Tirum Gem, Titangem, Titania Brilliante, Titania Midnight Stone, Titanium, Titanium Rutile, Titanstone and Zaba Gem. 'Rainbow Gem' perhaps comes nearest to an advertising man's description. Rutile was important as the first truly new gem in modern jewellery.

Rutile melts at $1925°C$ and is conveniently grown by the Verneuil flame fusion technique. The original experiments used an oxyacetylene torch with two nozzles inclined at $45°$ [1]. The major problem faced by the crystal grower is that molten rutile tends to lose oxygen, so that the titanium to oxygen ratio is not the ideal 2:1 but may increase to, say, 2.02:1. Oxygen-deficient rutile is not colourless but is black or very dark blue, and the clear stones required for gem applications are produced by heating the dark crystals in an oxidising atmosphere for a few hours at $800-1200°C$. Even after this oxidation process, rutile is not perfectly colourless but has a pale 'straw' yellow tint. The loss of oxygen during growth of the boule can be reduced by the use of a 3-tube burner, introduced by Leon Merker of National Lead Industries of Amboy, New Jersey. As in the case of ruby, the rutile powder is carried down the oxygen stream in the central tube, but around the tube a separate flow of oxygen is maintained to provide an oxidising atmosphere and so to decrease the tendency of the boule to be reduced by hydrogen from the intermediate tube. The presence of two reaction zones increases the turbulence in the flame and so gives a constant temperature zone over a wider region. The titanium oxide powder is prepared by heating ammonium titanium sulphate and must be fine and free-flowing, as for the synthesis of ruby or spinel. A very sensitive hopper with a vibrator drive has been found to be better than the hammer introduced by Verneuil. The vibration results in a more even flow of powder and so eliminates the periodic cooling of the crystal surface due to the arrival of a 'batch' of powder. It is this irregularity in powder flow which gives rise to the strained layer structures characteristic of crystals grown by the Verneuil method (Verneuil himself had thought that the layer structure was essential). A motor drive has replaced hand lowering of the crystals which was the technique of the early flame fusion apparatus. Accurate control of the gas flows, together with a straight spindle for the crystal to grow on, are further essentials for good quality crystals. Crystals are typically grown to a size of 20 grams (100 carats).

Various patents [3] have described the production of coloured rutile. It is reported that the addition of niobium pentoxide Nb_2O_5 in a concentration of 0.05%, of gallium oxide Ga_2O_3 or of aluminium oxide Al_2O_3 between 0.005% and 0.05%, produce a more nearly colourless crystal. On the other hand, the addition of chromium oxide Cr_2O_3 or of vanadium oxide V_2O_5 in a concentration of about 1% produces a red colouration. Cobalt oxide CoO gives a yellow colour at low concentrations (0.005%–0.05%), but an amber stone at moderate concentrations (0.1%) and a reddish-amber if the concentration is increased to 0.13%. Nickel oxide NiO also gives a yellow stone at similarly low concentrations, amber when it is added at concentrations between 0.05 and 0.1% and deep red at 0.1 to 0.13%. The addition of molybdenum, tungsten, uranium or beryllium oxides is reported to give bluish-white rutile when the concentration is below 0.005%. Increasing the concentration of these **dopants** up to 1% can produce light or dark blue stones, while blue-black stones are obtained with higher concentrations.

The National Lead company also produced star rutile [4] by adding magnesium oxide in a concentration of 0.2 to 1%. The asterism is obtained by heating the oxidised boule to between 1100° and 1500°C to precipitate the MgO or some magnesium titanate as small crystals. The resulting star rutiles have not been as popular as star sapphires and rubies, and not even the coloured stones are readily available now, except possibly in Japan.

Colourless rutile has kept some popularity but is now seen in rings relatively rarely. One of the disadvantages of this material, besides its softness, is the difficulty of removing the yellow colouration. Exactly why rutile retains its pale straw colour even when its oxygen content approaches the 'ideal' value for TiO_2 is not known, but this colour must be due either to a very small residual concentration of Ti^{3+} ions or to other defects called **colour centres**.

In principle it should be possible to produce clear, colourless rutile crystals by the flux method at temperatures well below the melting point. In fact there have been many reports of the growth of rutile crystals from various fluxes, and the crystals are often colourless or almost so. The disadvantage of the flux method is that the rutile grows as needle-shaped crystals which are totally unsuitable for cutting as gemstones, although they may find alternative applications. The largest crystals grown to date measure 10 X 3 X 3 mm [5] and although much longer crystals have been grown, they are of smaller diameter.

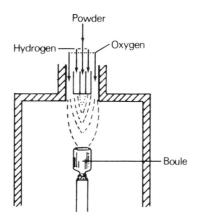

Fig. 5.1. 3-tube burner developed for the growth of rutile and strontium titanate.

STRONTIUM TITANATE

Strontium titanate was introduced by NL Industries in 1953 and it soon became established as the outstanding alternative to diamond, a position which it held for over a decade. The refractive index (2.41 compared with 2.42) is very close to that of diamond, and the dispersion is roughly four times larger. Unlike rutile, strontium titanate is isotropic so that there is no fuzziness in the appearance of the rear facets. As in the case of rutile, which it largely replaced, strontium titanate was offered to the public under a great variety of names. The most popular have been 'Diagem' and 'Fabulite' but some of the lesser known alternatives are [2] Bal de Feu, Diamontina, Dynagem, Jewelite, Kenneth Lane Jewel, Lustigem, Marvelite, Rossini Jewel, Sorella, Pauline Trigere, Wellington and Zenithite.

Like rutile, strontium titanate is brittle and may crack if subject to stress. It's advantage over rutile is that it can be made perfectly colourless, but it shares the disadvantage that its hardness is low for cutting as a facetted stone. Because facet corners tend to wear very quickly, gemstones have been marketed in which a 'crown' of sapphire or spinel is placed over a base or 'pavilion' of strontium titanate, and the resulting 'doublets' combine the appearance of strontium titanate with the wear-resistance of a much harder stone. These otherwise excellent diamond replacements have only one disadvantage; the ideal adhesive for joining the two sections has not yet been found, and that used may discolour with age. Emprezo de Couto of Kobe, Japan have developed a technique of fusing the crown to the pavilion of their 'Diamontina' doublets but I have not seen a sample of these.

Strontium titanate is grown in the Verneuil oxyhydrogen furnace, using a 3-tube burner as for rutile [6]. The melting point is 2050°C, and the flame is maintained at a temperature between 2110° and 2130°C. Typical flow rates are 4 litres per minute of oxygen through the inner tube, 5 litres per minute through the outer oxygen tube, and 40 litres per minute of hydrogen. In the actual growth of the crystal [6], the oxygen flow rate is varied to control the temperature while the hydrogen flow is maintained at a constant and relatively fast rate. Seed crystals are used as an alternative to selecting a crystallite in a powder cone. The seed is centred by moving the pedestal, and then the flow of powder is started and the oxygen rate increased until it reaches a value of ⅕ th the rate of the hydrogen. After the boule has reached a diameter of around 12 mm (½ inch), the powder flow is increased with the gas flow held constant, and the pedestal is lowered. Crystals are grown up to 20 grams in weight, a length of about 35 mm, and then lowered 5 to 7 mm to cool the crystal slightly prior to a longer cooling in the furnace enclosure with the gases shut off. The powder used to grow the crystals is made by heating strontium titanate oxalate with strontium chloride at 500°C or above to yield particles sized between 0.1 to 0.3 μm. The crystals are black as they leave the furnace but become colourless on heating in an oxidising atmosphere for 12 to 180 hours at temperatures in the range from 1700° to 650°C. If an excess of strontium oxide is added, this helps the formation of perfectly colourless crystals. Hans Scheel of the IBM Zurich Laboratory has found [7] that the excess of strontium required depends on the crystal growth rate, and has grown high quality crystals by adding 3.8% excess of strontium carbonate to the starting powder and using a growth rate of 20 to 26 mm per hour. Crystals 1.5 cm in diameter and 3 cm long were grown, and various investigators have given a review of flame fusion growth of strontium titanate.

Strontium titanate may be coloured by adding various elements [8]. As seen in Table 5.2, the range of colours which has been achieved is not wide, and the colourless stones have been most in demand.

Strontium titanate can also be prepared by the flux method, the aim being to grow crystals of greater perfection than is possible in the Verneuil furnace. Such experiments are motivated by the scientific interest in strontium titanate, which undergoes an unusual structure transformation on cooling to low temperatures. Defects in the crystal influence the measurements of physical properties, and may mask the true effects which are to be studied. The most nearly perfect crystals of this material produced to date were grown from fluxes of potassium fluoride mixed with lithium fluoride, or from strontium borate with lithium borate [7]. Crystals up to 12 X 11 X 9 mm were produced, but this required a growth period of about 11 weeks. Unlike the crystals grown in the Verneuil oxyhydrogen furnace, these crystals are truly isotropic in their optical properties whereas the flame fusion-grown crystals show slight birefringence due to strain introduced in the growth process.

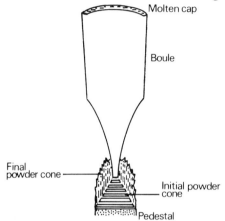

Fig. 5.2. Strontium titanate boule showing the build-up of the powder cone before and during the growth of the boule.

Table 5.2 Colours of strontium titanate

Element	0.001–0.005	0.005–0.02	0.02–0.1	0.1–3
		% oxide added		
Chromium	yellow to dark brown	dark-red to red brown to black	black	black
Cobalt	–	yellow to topaz	topaz to reddish-topaz	deep red to reddish-black
Iron	–	yellow to yellow-brown	brown	dark red-brown to black
Manganese	–	yellow	yellow-orange to deep reddish-orange	deep red to reddish-black
Nickel	–	yellow to topaz	topaz to reddish-topaz	deep red to reddish-black
Vanadium	yellow to dark red-brown	dark red-brown to black	black	black

The cost of the flux-grown materials is inevitably rather high because of the slow rate of growth, and stones of acceptable quality for gem applications can be produced much more economically by the flame fusion process. The flux method comes into its own mainly for the production of more highly valued gemstones, and where it can produce crystals more closely resembling the natural material.

GARNETS

Naturally-occurring garnets are complex oxides of silicon -silicates, such as $Mg_3Al_2Si_3O_{12}$ (pyrope garnet). The most familiar garnets are reddish-brown in colour, although there is also an attractive green variety called demantoid garnet. There is no naturally occurring colourless garnet because, although the ideal pyrope garnet would be colourless, in practice all garnets contain iron, and this is responsible for the red colour.

Colourless garnets can be synthesised because the iron and other colouring elements may be eliminated, and these have been the most popular alternatives to diamond in recent years. Although crystals of the silicate garnets can be prepared, molten silicates are viscous and have a tendency to form glasses on cooling. Hence the crystal grower finds it more convenient to replace the silicon by aluminium and the magnesium by some trivalent element such as yttrium. Yttrium aluminium garnet, $Y_3Al_5O_{12}$, has enjoyed quite a lengthy reign as the most popular synthetic colourless stone.

Purists maintain that such materials should not be called garnets, because natural garnets contain silicon. However their crystal structure is identical to that of the natural garnets, and the 'garnet' nomenclature has been accepted by the scientific community and, if reluctantly, by most gemmologists.

It was the magnetic properties of yttrium iron garnet (YIG) which first attracted the interest of scientists. Iron garnets are perhaps the most important members of that class of magnetic materials called the ferites, which are strongly magnetic but electrically insulating. They have been extensively employed in communications and as 'bubble' domain films are likely to be used even more widely as storage elements in computers, calculators and telephone systems.

Gemmologically iron garnets are of little interest because, although thin films of YIG are green in colour, bulk crystals are invariably black. The first patents for the growth of garnet crystals [9] were awarded in the early 1960's to Jim Nielsen and Joe Remeika of the Bell Laboratories. They grew yttrium iron garnet from a lead oxide flux or from mixtures of lead oxide with lead fluoride or boric oxide. Interest in yttrium aluminium garnet (YAG) also began in the early 1960's, when the suitability of this material for use in lasers was noted. The first crystals were grown by the flux method but larger crystals can be produced at a much faster rate, and more economically, by pulling from the melt.

Although YAG's refractive index and dispersion are both appreciably lower than those of diamond, they are sufficiently close to make this garnet a most acceptable replacement for it. YAG has the additional advantage that it takes a high polish. On the whole, YAG has enjoyed a remarkable success, being the first synthetic diamond substitute to penetrate the very conservative London jewellery market. Part of this success may be attributed to the publicity given to Cartier's 'Diamonaire' replica of the famous 69.42 carat pear-shaped diamond which Richard Burton gave to Elizabeth Taylor. This diamond, normally worn as a pendant, was bought in 1969 for over $1,000,000. The insurance for wearing the real stone for a single evening will be in the region of $1,000, while the replica cost only $3,500, or about £2,000. It is not difficult to spot the diamond when it is placed beside its replica, but only an expert can detect the synthetic stone when the two are separated. So it was the film star set who increased the market for diamond simulations, and manufacturers can thank the burglars (or insurance companies) for helping to promote their products.

The largest manufacturer of YAG is the Airtron division of Litton Industries in Morris Plains, New Jersey, who first marketed their stones in October 1969. Their trade name of 'Diamonaire' is often used as synonymous with YAG, but a number of other manufacturers, mainly in the USA, also market (or have marketed) the stones. They do so under a variety of trade names, for example Diamone, Diamonique, Diamonte, Di'YAG, Geminair, Linde Simulated Diamond, Regalaire, and even the ingenious Triamond. YAG is marketed for about $1/20$ th of the cost of an average quality diamond. Of course this does not mean that a ring containing a YAG stone will cost twenty times less than a diamond ring, because the cost of the ring itself and of the workmanship in fitting the stone are the same in both cases. However, a purchaser may prefer to spend his money on a much larger YAG stone rather than a small diamond.

The YAG crystals from which gemstones are cut are mainly grown by the Czochralski process of pulling from the melt. A seed crystal is inserted into an iridium crucible until it just contacts a melt weighing around 2 kg. This is heated to a temperature around 2000°C (just above its melting point) by a radio-frequency generator producing several kilowatts of power. The crystal is pulled out of the melt at a steady rate and the temperature of the melt is varied in such a way that the diameter increases regularly until it reaches a value of around 1½ inches, at which it is maintained constant. Crystals may be up to 1 foot in length. The whole process is semi-automatic, with the diameter of the growing crystals controlled by position sensors. These normally work on the principle that the miniscus of liquid around the solid crystal emits more infra-red radiation than the solid or the flat liquid surface, so that any variation in the position of this bright ring will be sensed by an infra-red detector.

Several crystal pullers can be maintained by a single operator and cost effectiveness is vital to a producer's success, because the large number of actual and potential manufacturers ensures that competition is severe. I visited the production facility at the Airtron plant in 1972, where I was allowed into the locked room where YAG crystals are grown only after it had been noted that I was with the manager, Don Lepore. Airtron, and presumably other US producers, were most afraid of Japanese competition and my chances of a tour of the production furnaces would have been slim had I been a Japanese industrialist! One factor has favoured American manufacturers; the original development cost of YAG production was largely met from government funds because of the demand for crystals for use in lasers. The application of YAG as a gemstone developed very much as a sideline to scientific interest in this material as a laser crystal.

Coloured YAGs can be produced by adding suitable dopants. Laser crystals normally contain the rare earth neodymium, which gives a pleasant lilac colour similar to, but easily distinguished from, that of amethyst. Most other rare earth elements give a yellow or yellow-green coloration, although erbium gives a pink and praesodymium a pale green stone. Cobalt with silicon gives a clear blue colour, manganese a pink or red, and titanium a yellow. Most interest has probably been aroused by chromium-doping of YAG, because chromium produces an attractive green material which is arguably the most attractive green gemstone, natural or synthetic, apart from emerald. Although not unknown, bright green garnets are rare in nature and these synthetic green garnets would probably become very popular if they were more widely known. A variety of coloured YAGs are available from retailers.

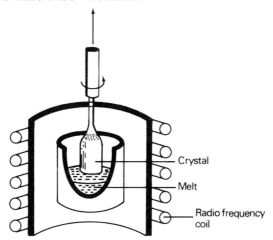

Fig. 5.3. Diagram of the arrangement used for pulling crystals such as YAG from the melt.

Garnets grown by the flux method are often more strongly coloured than those grown by pulling from the melt, because the crystal will accept a higher concentration of dopant when it is grown more slowly at a lower temperature. Flux-grown garnets normally cannot be produced at a rate much faster than about 1 mm per day, whereas growth from the melt can proceed at several mm per hour. Flux-grown crystals may contain inclusions, which are the curse of crystal growers but are often beloved by gemmologists because the stones then cut resemble more closely the products of nature!

Gadolinium gallium garnet, often abbreviated to GGG, is another colourless garnet which has made an impact on the gemmological scene following intensive interest in it for scientific applications. In this material, the yttrium of YAG is replaced by the rare earth element gadolinium (symbol Gd)* and the aluminium by gallium (symbol Ga) so that its formula is $Gd_3Ga_5O_{12}$. Scientific interest in GGG has arisen mainly because its lattice constant is very close to that of yttrium iron garnet YIG. A **lattice constant** is the length of the so-called crystallographic unit cell, the smallest unit of the cubic

*Gadolinium is named after the Finnish chemist Johannes Gadolin, who discovered the element yttrium.

garnet lattice which is repeated in three dimensions to form the crystal. Because of this, GGG provides a 'host' crystal onto which thin films of the magnetic YIG may be depositied. These films are used for magnetic 'bubble' memory devices, mentioned briefly in the first Chapter, and the close match between the crystal lattices of the magnetic YIG and the non-magnetic GGG is a necessary requirement if the film is to be of good quality, without serious strain or cracks.

The possibilities of GGG as a gemstone were realised when its optical properties were measured. Its refractive index, though below that of diamond, is apparently higher than that of YAG and its dispersion of 0.038 cannot be distinguished by eye from that of diamond. Like YAG it takes a good polish, and a side-by-side comparison of cut stones shows that GGG is the more attractive gemstone. Unfortunately its hardness is quoted as only 6½ [10], which means that it will not retain its attractiveness as a facetted stone over long periods of use. Another disadvantage GGG shares with YAG is a tendency to pick up dust, leading to loss of sparkle. Hence they require cleaning more often than most stones. GGG may be rather brittle, another disadvantage because the edges of cut stones can be damaged more easily than is the case with most stones.

A serious problem which was encountered during the early stages of GGG production was its tendency to discolour in sunlight. Although the stone can be prepared in a perfectly colourless form, it tends to develop a brown coloration due to the formation of **colour centres**. This does not seem to have been widely noted in the gemmoligical literature, although some stones were reported to have a brownish tinge. The origin of the colour centre was found to be associated with a very small departure of the gadolinium to gallium ratio from the ideal value of 3:5, due to evaporation of gallium oxide. However it has now been found possible to correct this fault, either by changing the atmosphere used during crystal growth, or by adding a small quantity of a suitable dopant. Like YAG, GGG is grown by the Czochralski process, and is now produced in a number of laboratories. As a matter of routine, the larger producers now grow crystals 3 inch in diameter, and of very high quality, for the electronics industry. The growth of GGG for the gem trade is mainly in the hands of smaller specialist producers such as Deltronic Crystal Industries of Denville and Synthetic Crystal Products Corp. of Lake Hopatcong, both in New Jersey, The location of these companies is no coincidence because their respective founders, Stuart Samuelson and Edward Comperchio, were both previously employed in that part of the electronics industry which is concentrated in a narrow belt of New Jersey. The unfortunate lack of hardness may prevent the sale of cut stones on a large scale, but only time will tell whether the marketing agencies need to dream up yet another set of exciting names. The only one reported so far is 'Galliant'.

GGG is more expensive to produce than YAG, partly because the raw materials, gadolinium oxide and gallium oxide, are themselves substantially dearer than their counterparts used in the making of YAG. A report by Robert Crowningshield in the Winter 1973/74 issue of *Gems and Gemmology* suggested that it would not be marketed both because of its high cost and the declining interest in diamond replacements. At present there is little evidence to suggest that GGG will rival YAG's former popularity, although it is a welcome addition to the materials available to lapidarists. Coloured crystals are obtained by doping GGG, green stones being produced by cobalt addition and red by manganese.

This by no means exhausts the family of colourless synthetic garnets and the other obvious combinations, yttrium gallium garnet $Y_3Ga_5O_{12}$ and gadolinium aluminium garnet $Gd_3Al_5O_{12}$, have also been prepared and found to have similar properties to YAG and GGG. The garnet family has not been searched exhaustively for the best alternative to diamond, and garnets may well have more to offer the gemmologist. However, at present all the indications are that garnets, and indeed any other diamond simulants, are likely to be eclipsed by a relatively new material on the gem scene, cubic zirconia. On the other hand, they are expected to keep some part of the market, because YAG in particular will probably remain appreciably cheaper than cubic zirconia.

CUBIC ZIRCONIA

YAG became less popular in the mid-1970's, to some extent because it was replaced by GGG, although its decline in popularity seemed to be independent of the appearance of a superior alternative. However 1976 saw the 'arrival' of a new transparent material which seems destined to be the outstanding man-made alternative to diamond, at least in the forseeable future [11, 12].

Cubic stabilized zirconia (CSZ or CZ) has a refractive index of 2.17 to 2.18, which is close enough to the 2.42 of diamond to make it difficult to distinguish between them by eye. The same is almost true of GGG, with a refractive index of 2.02, but at 1.83 YAG is sufficiently different for a simple visual test to detect that it is not diamond. The dispersion is 0.060 against diamond's 0.044, which again is so close that it takes an instrument rather than the eye to tell the difference. The differences both in refracting index and dispersion can be minimized in cut stones by changing the proportions of the crown angles. CZ takes a good polish and has a hardness similar to that of YAG, so that it is hard enough to give a long life even in rings. At around 5.65 the relative density is much higher than that of diamond, but this test can only be applied when the stone is removed from its setting. Since the refractive index is beyond the range of gemmological refractometers, there is no traditional test which jewellers can use to distinguish zirconia from diamond when the stone is set in a ring and even careful jewellers may make mistakes in identification. Inclusions have been observed in some CZ crystals, but these would not be present in better quality material. The best test relates to the high density of CZ, because diamonds are extremely transparent to X-rays. If rings containing diamond and its various simulants are placed on photographic film and irradiated with X-rays, the diamond will transmit X-rays much better than the other stones. Hence the blackening of the film below the diamond will be much greater than that below the other stones, over a wide range of exposure times. CZ is also much less transparent to ultra-violet light than diamond, or many other simulants.

Since CZ is such a good alternative to diamond, the reader may well ask why it was not available earlier. The main reason lies in its high melting point, which is well above 2000°C and not easily reached with the flame fusion furnace. The manufacture of this material is complicated by the **polymorphism** of zirconia – its existence in various different crystal structures. Pure zirconia, the stable oxide of zirconium (ZrO_2), has a monoclinic crystal structure at room temperature but transforms on heating above 1250°C to a tetragonal structure. A hexagonal structure may occur around 1900°C and only above 2300°C does the structure of ZrO_2 become cubic. When this cubic zirconia is cooled, however, it reverts back to the monoclinic form. In order to prepare cubic zirconia stable at room temperature, a **stabilizing** material such as magnesium oxide MgO, yttrium oxide Y_2O_3, or calcium oxide CaO must be added. The formula of one gem material is typically $Zr_{0.842} Y_{0.158} O_{1.92}$. The deficiency in oxygen compared to ZrO_2 is important because it makes CZ a fairly good conductor of electricity at high temperatures.

The so-called stabilized zirconia ceramics have been known for some time and have a variety of uses in high temperature construction. These ceramic materials are opaque and white. As is frequently the case, the application of CZ in gemmology requires the growth of single crystals and these are much more difficult to produce than the ceramic material. In fact the growth of large crystals of cubic zirconia was achieved only by the introduction of a new technique called **skull melting**. This method of growing crystals from the melt was developed in 1973 by V. V. Osiko, V. I. Alexandrov and collaborators [13] at the Lebedev Physical Institute in Moscow. The essence of the method is a **cold crucible** which is maintained at room temperature by a flow of water through tubes which make up the **skull**. A radio-frequency generator supplies enough energy to zirconia powder inside the crucible to melt the centre of the sample while leaving the outside cool and therefore solid. The molten zirconia is therefore surrounded by a crust of powder of the same material. This is important for the growth of CZ crystals because it is extremely difficult to find a container for zirconia at its high melting point; containers will either react with the zirconia or melt themselves.

The cold crucible or skull must be carefully designed if the high-frequency radiation is to penetrate into the zirconia while leaving the skull itself cold. The skull is closed at the bottom, and the sides are made up of parallel hollow copper fingers cooled by a flow of water inside. It is made in halves and is open to the surrounding air at the top.

The transfer of energy from the radio-frequency generator to the zirconia is by radiation from a coil surrounding the crucible. The energy transfer is only effective if the material conducts electricity, which zirconia does at high temperatures. In order to make the sample conducting at lower temperatures some zirconium metal is added. This oxidises as the sample heats up, by reaction with oxygen in the air, and so becomes part of the zirconium oxide charge. The sample also contains the CaO or Y_2O_3 to stabilize the cubic crystal structure.

Transfer of power to the sample continues until all the charge is melted apart from a thin skin in close contact with the skull. In order to grow the crystals, the power to the radio-frequency heating coil is slowly reduced. Solidification proceeds from the base of the

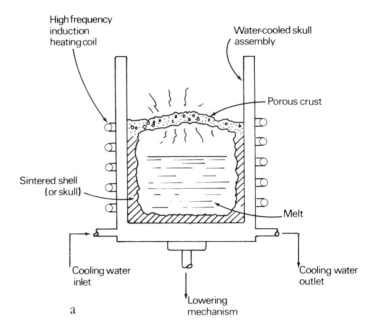

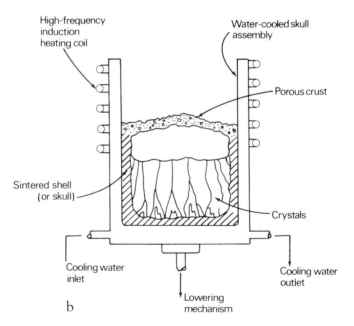

Fig. 5.4. (a) Crucible used for skull melting of cubic zirconia.
(b) Arrangement of crystals inside the skull after cooling.

Fig. 5.5. Crystal of cubic zirconia grown by skull melting.

skull, although a crust also forms on top of the melt at an early stage. Columnar crystals up to 2 cm in diameter and of similar length can be separated from the solidified mass after cooling to room temperature. Yellow, red, lilac, brown and presumably other coloured crystals can be produced, but the most popular material is likely to be the diamond-like clear crystal with a slight yellowish tinge.

At present, CZ is being produced by the Lebedev Institute in the USSR and since 1976 has been marketed under the name 'Phianite'. CZ is also produced, as 'Djevalite', by Djevahirdjian, better known for their production of corundum and spinel by the flame fusion process, and by the Ceres Corporation of Waltham, Massachusetts ('Diamonesque'). The skull melting apparatus is produced in the United States by Intermat Corporation, a division of Arthur D. Little Inc. It was developed there under Joseph F. Wenckus, who is now president of Ceres Corp. Present expansion plans at Ceres include the introduction of a 150 kw power supply, which will permit growth charges of 100 lb.

Other companies will certainly wish to enter the growing market for CZ and new manufacturers are expected to announce their production of this material in the near future. Deltronic Inc. advertised CZ in the April 1978 issue of the Lapidary Journal. Other techniques will be tried to reduce cost and to improve the yield of gem quality material. Flux growth is possible, because several molten salt solvents have been tried for the crystal growth of CZ, but the slow growth rate is a handicap in a commercial process where there is competition with melt growth. Alternative means of producing high temperatures, such as high intensity lamps and lasers or ionized plasmas, may be tried. The likely popularity of CZ is also expected to lead to the study of alternative materials of very high melting point as possible diamond substitutes.

YTTRIUM ALUMINATE

If yttrium oxide Y_2O_3 and aluminium oxide Al_2O_3 are combined in a 1:1 ratio rather than the 3:5 ratio required to make YAG, the resulting compound is yttrium aluminate $YAlO_3$. This material has also been investigated as a possible laser crystal and, like YAG, is a candidate as a diamond substitute. Its hardness is similar to that of YAG and its refractive index is rather higher, but it is doubly refracting because the crystal structure is orthorhombic and not cubic. The dispersion has not yet been reported in the gemmological literature but it is likely to be similar to that of YAG.

There do not appear to have been any systematic studies of the colour of doped yttrium aluminates. However, a bright red stone, presumably doped with chromium, has been reported in the gemmological literature [14].

YTTRIUM OXIDE

Yttrium oxide Y_2O_3 is itself potentially an attractive diamond replacement. Single crystals are extremely difficult to prepare because of the high melting point, which is well in excess of 2000°C. In 1970 a material named yttralox appeared on the US gem scene [15]. This is a ceramic material produced by heating powdered Y_2O_3 with a few percent of thorium oxide ThO_2 while at the same time applying a very high pressure produced by a hydraulic press. This hot pressing process results in an optically clear material which is of use to the scientific community as lenses and other optical components capable of withstanding very high temperatures.

The refractive index of Yttralox is 1.92, higher than YAG, and at 0.039 the dispersion is very close to that of diamond. On the debit side the hardness of the material is too low, and, as mentioned in the Introduction, it is not possible to achieve a brilliance comparable with that of single crystals with non-crystalline materials.

NIOBATES

Another crystal produced for scientific applications but marketed in the USA as a gemstone is lithium niobate, $LiNbO_3$, which appears under the trade name of 'Linobate'. Single crystals are grown by the Czochralski method of pulling from the melt, the melting point having the relatively low value of 1250°C.

Although lithium niobate is doubly refracting, at 2.30 its refractive index is close to that of a diamond. The dispersion is 0.120, nearly three times that of diamond but still lower than that of strontium titanate. Apart from a 'fuzzy' appearance due to the rather high birefringence, with a hardness of only 5½ 'Linobate' has one of the lowest values of any diamond substitute. 'Linobate' is the trade name of Crystal Technology Inc. of Mountain View, California, a company which Frank Halden and Walter Nelson formed in 1968 to produce lithium niobate and ruby, mainly for the scientific community. More recently they have grown YAG, GGG and lithium tantalate, partly for sale to lapidarists.

Coloured stones have been produced, green crystals being obtained by chromium doping and red crystals by using iron. Cobalt produces a violet or blue colour, while manganese or nickel are used for yellow stones.

Although both colourless and coloured stones have apparently long been popular in the USA, they are little known in Britain and have not made the same impact as strontium titanate or YAG in Europe generally.

Lithium niobate is only one of a range of refractory niobates which have been studied extensively because of their dielectric or optical properties. In general these are doubly refracting because cubic crystals are unsuitable for the main applications, which concern the use of lasers in communications and for a range of other purposes. One of these materials is potassium niobate with some niobium replaced by tantalum -potassium tantalate-niobate $KTa_xNb_{1-x}O_3$, normally abbreviated to KTN. Cut stones have appeared on the gemmological scene [16] and are reported to have the high refractive index of 2.27. Although the dispersion has not been reported, the family of niobates appear to have a high dispersion and the crystal, grown by the pulling method, certainly look attractive. The hardness of KTN is only just over 6, which will prevent its winning great popularity as a gemstone.

Another very attractive member of this class of materials is barium sodium niobate $Ba_2NaNb_3O_{15}$, known to the scientific community as 'banana'. Uncut, as they are grown, the crystals are of striking appearance and the dispersion is probably higher than that of diamond, although it may not have been measured. The refractive index is 2.31 and cut stones are very attractive. 'Banana' is unlikely to be grown for gem purposes because it is not one of the easier members of the niobate family to prepare as high quality crystals. However, good quality crystals are now grown by Larry Rothrock and his colleagues at Union Carbide Crystal Products division in San Diego.

TITANATES

Strontium titanate $Sr TiO_3$ is by far the best-known titanate in the gemmological field but it is only one of a series of compounds which includes barium and calcium titanates $BaTiO_3$ and $CaTiO_3$ as well. These have also been cut as gemstones and have properties which are similar to those of strontium titanate. They suffer from the disadvantage of being rather more difficult to prepare as single crystals. Barium titanate decomposes on melting, and crystals can be pulled only from a melt which contains an excess of titanium oxide. This difference in composition, during crystal growth, between the crystal and the melt has the effect of slowing down the rate of growth and so the crystals cannot be prepared so economically as can strontium titanate. Barium and calcium titanates both have a refractive index of 2.40 [16], close to that of diamond, but the hardness is only 6 to 6½ for $BaTiO_3$ and probably below 6 for $CaTiO_3$.

BROMELLITE

Bromellite is the mineralogical name for beryllium oxide BeO. Although it has never been anything but a rarity in gemmology, bromellite is mentioned in reviews of gemstones, and cut stones have been seen in gemmological laboratories. Bromellite crystals have been grown by the flux method, particularly by Stan Austerman of Rockwell International, Anaheim, California. They have been used as heat sinks for semiconductors. As a gemstone bromellite has the advantage of a hardness of 9, but the refractive index is only 1.728 and the crystals are birefringent. The main objection to the use of bromellite for any application is its very high toxicity, which is a problem both for the crystal grower and for the lapidarist in cutting and polishing the stones.

MAGNESIUM OXIDE

In conclusion, mention should be made of magnesium oxide MgO, which is sometimes referred to by its mineralogical name periclase. This material is not an outstanding substitute for diamond but receives occasional mention in the gemmological literature because cut stones have appeared in jewellery submitted for inspection by the gem testing laboratories. The refractive index is 1.737 and the dispersion also appears low to the eye, although a figure is not readily available. The hardness is only 5 on the Mohs scale, which is extremely low for a facetted stone.

WHICH IS THE BEST ALTERNATIVE TO DIAMOND?

No gemstone can match diamond for hardness, but many synthetics have similar or even more exciting optical properties. Rutile and barium titanate both have high refractive indices, the former even higher than that of diamond, but the brilliance of rutile is offset by its yellow coloration. Both these stones have a very high dispersion and that of rutile is probably too high for the average consumer because it gives the stone a 'flashy' appearance. Strontium titanate has a lower refractive index but its dispersion, while still high enough to give it an attractive appearance, is substantially lower than that of rutile. Strontium titanate has the additional advantage over rutile and barium titanate that it is optically isotropic, and its appearance is enhanced by the resulting sharpness of the black edges as seen through the stone. Strontium titanate would therefore be a leading contender but for its rather low refractive index, not to mention its hardness. It is really too soft for regular wear in rings, or even in other jewellery where abrasion is less likely.

Sapphire and spinel are too dull, and so YAG with its reasonably high dispersion and moderate refractive index has until recently been the success of the 1970's, compensating by its hardness for its modest fire and brilliance compared with that of diamond. GGG has superior optical properties and could become successful as a gemstone, but it is more expensive than YAG and probably would not be able to take sufficient trade, from YAG on the one hand and diamond on the other, to be a good commercial proposition. Cubic zirconia seems destined to take the largest share of the market for diamond sub-stitutes. Of the long-established synthetics, strontium titanate has kept a share of the market and would be more popular if the problem of its hardness could be solved. Ideally, it should be possible to apply a hard coating which will adhere firmly to a titanate without affecting its brilliance. At least one patent does exist for coating softer gem-stones with corundum [17], the coating being applied from a vapour rich in aluminium and oxygen at around 500°C, followed by heat treatment at 900–1000°C. If this process were wholly successful, it would result in an outstanding transparent gemstone at a reasonable price. However, it is unlikely that a hard, crystalline coating would adhere to all facets without cracks or visible imperfections. A nearly perfect coating is generally possible only when there is a good fit between the actual atoms of the coating material and those in the crystal below. The absence of coated stones from the gem scene is evidence for the presumed lack of success of this patent, at least for strontium titanate. For the present, therefore, a doublet with a strontium titanate base and a corundum (sapphire) crown is one of the most attractive man-made alternatives to diamond, with the one handicap of uncertainty in the effect on the adhesive of prolonged exposure to light.

So the diamond simulant of the moment is clearly cubic zirconia, which is a convincing substitute in all respects except hardness. It is remarkable that, although at the time of writing cubic zirconia has been known as a gemstone for over a year, it is unknown to the general public. A massive advertising campaign might have been expected by now, but we are still waiting for it. I have even heard it suggested that the absence of publicity can be explained by a sinister reason: that cubic zirconia is *so* good a simulant that unsuspecting purchasers are buying it as 'diamond' and professional jewellers can't tell the difference! However, this explanation is unlikely because it would imply criminal fraud on the part of major distributors, and in fact several tests can be applied to distinguish the zirconia from diamond. The only major disadvantage of cubic zirconia is its high melting point, which makes it difficult to grow.

As large diamonds of good quality become ever more scarce, simulants will probably become more popular than at any time in the past.

REFERENCES

[1]   C. H. Moore, *Amer. Assoc. Min. Engrs. Trans.*, **184** (1949) 194.

[2]   Anon., *Gems & Gemology,* **13** (1970/71) 245.

[3]   W. G. Eversole & W. Derst (Union Carbide), U.S. Pat. 2,693,421 (Nov. 2, 1954); L. Merker (National Lead), U. S. Pats. 2,715,071 (Aug. 9, 1955), 2,763,558 (Sept. 18, 1956) and 2,801,182 (July 30, 1957).

[4]   L. Merker, U.S. Pat. 2,760,874 (Aug. 18, 1956).

[5]   E. A. D. White, *Jnl. Materials Science,* **1** (1966) 199.

[6]   L. Merker, U.S. Pat. 2,764,490 (Sept. 25, 1956); *Trans. Amer. Inst. Min. Met. Eng.* **202** (1955) 645.

[7]   H. J. Scheel, *Proc. 3rd European Conf. of Ferroelectricity,* Zurich, 1975; J. G. Bednorz & H. J. Scheel, *Jnl. of Crystal Growth,* **41** (1977) 5.

[8]   L. Merker, U.S. Pat. 2,723,915 (Nov. 15, 1955).

[9]   J. W. Nielsen, U.S. Pat. 2,957,827 (Oct. 25, 1960) and U.S. Pat. 3,050,407 (Aug. 21, 1962); J. P. Remeika, U.S. Pat. 3,079,240 (Feb. 26, 1963).

[10] R. Webster, *J. Gemmology,* **14** (1974) 115.

[11] K. Nassau, *Lapidary Journal,* **3** (1977) 18.

[12] A. Hodgkinson, *Retail Jeweller,* 18th August 1977.

[13] V. I. Alexandrov, V. V. Osiko, A. M. Prokhorov & V. M. Tatarinsev, *Vestnik. Akad. Nauk. SSSR,* **12** (1973) 29.

[14] R. Crowningshield, *Gems & Gemology,* **13** (1971) 344.

[15] R. Crowningshield, *Gems & Gemology,* **13** (1970) 192.

[16] R. Webster, *J. Gemmology,* **12** (1970) 101.

[17] S. E. Mayer, U.S. Pat. 3,539,379 (Nov. 10, 1970).

CHAPTER 6

The Silica Family

The silica family comprises an amazing variety of gemstones. In addition to the colourless form known as rock crystal, there is the purple amethyst, the yellow or brown citrine, the dark brown cairngorm or smoky quartz, the pink 'rose quartz' and the brown tiger's eye with its asbestos inclusions. The varieties of quartz are all crystalline forms of the mineral silica or silicon dioxide SiO_2, with different types of impurity responsible for the various colours. Although the word 'quartz' strictly refers only to the single crystal form, silica also occurs as aggregates of microcrystals forming materials which have a milky translucency but which are not transparent. This latter group includes a number of inexpensive stones such as agate, cornelian, chrysoprase, heliotrope, moss agate and onyx, all of which are popular with the amateur lapidarist. However the most highly valued and exciting silica gemstone is the unique opal, which should rightly be included on the short list of the world's most valuable stones because it can command prices comparable with those of diamond or ruby. The story of the synthesis of opal is one of the most fascinating in the development of man-made gemstones and will form the larger part of this Chapter.

QUARTZ

Interest in the crystallization of quartz really began during World War II. Quartz crystals possess the property of **piezoelectricity**, which means that they may be made to vibrate by the application of an alternating electric field. The vibration occurs at a fixed frequency, depending upon the size of the material, and a plate cut from a quartz crystal has a characteristic frequency which is stable within extremely narrow limits provided that the temperature of the quartz remains constant. Quartz therefore provides the essential component of 'crystal-controlled oscillators', which are very important in communications. For example, the carrier wavelength of a transmission must remain highly stable for good quality reception.* During the war, the demand for quartz crystals for military applications exceeded the supply, which was adversely affected by transport problems.

Crystal growers seeking the best method to prepare large and relatively perfect crystals took a hint from nature. If an alkali is added to water, the solubility of quartz is quite high at temperatures around 400°C. Quartz is normally grown by a technique which involves the use of a temperature gradient, with crystal seed plates located in the upper, cooler region of the solution and small pieces of quartz 'nutrient' in the lower, hotter section. The seed is typically kept at 360°C and the nutrient at 400°C, and the quantity of solution is carefully adjusted so that it completely fills the pressure vessel cavity at the temperature and pressure used for crystal growth. The nutrient pieces dissolve at the higher temperature and silica is transported by convection to the region where the crystals grow. The seed plates are cut perpendicular to the trigonal axis of quartz, which is the direction along which the rate of crystal growth is fastest. Crystals can be grown at a rate of about 1 mm per day. Eventually the crystal **caps over** to form a double pyramid, but growth is normally ended before this stage is reached because the pyramid habit faces grow at a much lower rate. When growth is stopped in this way, the crystals show a characteristic **cobbled** appearance which makes them easily identifiable before cutting. The irregular **cobbles** are associated with imperfections within the crystals and in principle provide a means of identifying synthetic quartz crystals even when cut. However, rather sophisticated techniques may be necessary to detect this defect structure unambiguously.

The high pressure vessel used for hydrothermal growth of quartz must be made from a strong steel alloy and must be able to withstand pressures of around one to two thousand atmospheres at 400°C. It must be resistant to chemical attack by the solution and it may be lined by a noble metal such as gold, silver or platinum. The pressure vessels, known as **autoclaves**, can be a foot or more in internal

*More recently, quartz crystals have been used in accurate electronic clocks and watches.

diameter and crystals up to tens of kg in weight are now grown in commercial production. Only rarely are synthetic quartz crystals cut as gemstones, because natural rock crystal is inexpensive.

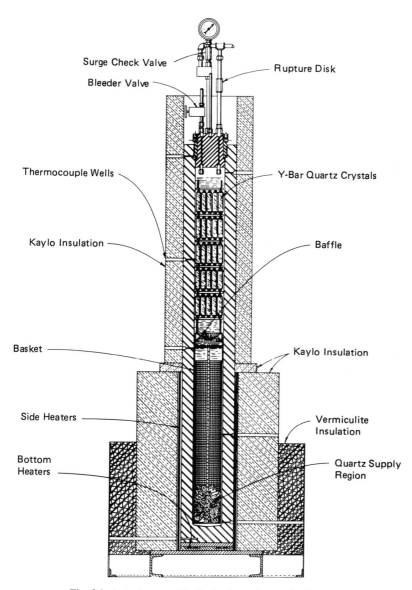

Fig. 6.1. Autoclave used for hydrothermal growth of quartz.

Until the present decade production of coloured quartz crystals proved difficult both because many metal salts are insoluble in alkaline solution, and because the growing crystals exhibited a strong tendency to reject any 'impurities', which therefore remained in the solution as growth proceeded. When potassium compounds were substituted for sodium ones in the water used as solvent, iron could be incorporated into the crystals, which became either green or brown in colour. These original colours were not very attractive, and the more desirable purple of amethyst could not be reproduced then.

In 1969 the noted gemmologist Basil Anderson [1] reported a pale blue quartz stone which had apparently originated in the Soviet Union, where hydrothermal quartz is grown on a large scale. The attractive blue colour is not found in nature and is due to the presence of cobalt. The same author's second report on blue quartz [2] mentioned a curious mottled effect when light was reflected onto the stone from a piece of white paper. This mottling may result from the cobbled structure caused by seeded growth.

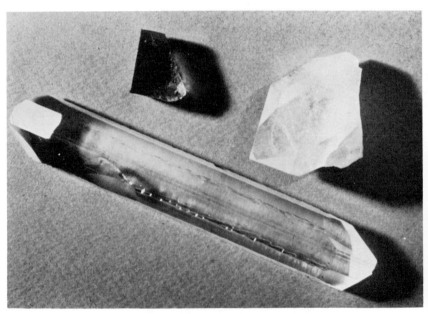

Fig. 6.2. Blue synthetic quartz with a colourless synthetic and a natural quartz crystal.

Sawyer Research Products of Ohio, USA began the production of coloured synthetic quartz at about the same time, and their materials

Fig. 5.6. Comparison of the most important crystals used as diamond simulants. *Top row:* (from left) Strontium titanate, cubic zircona, lithium niobate. *Middle row:* GGG, barium sodium niobate and lithium tantalate. *Bottom row:* Spinel and YAG.

Fig. 6.5. Gilson synthetic opals.

Fig. 6.6. The Slocum stone.

Fig. 7.6. Gilson turquoise.

enjoyed considerable popularity. The origin of colour in both natural and synthetic varieties of quartz has been intensively studied using the sophisticated techniques of solid state physics, such as electron spin resonance and nuclear magnetic resonance. In these, the material is placed in a strong magnetic field and is subjected to electromagnetic radiation at various frequencies. The specimen absorbs radiation at characteristic frequencies which depend upon the atom, its valence state (the number of electrons in the atom which are available to form chemical bonds) and its location in the crystal lattice.

Table 6.1 summarises the conclusions reached by recent studies of the origin of colours in quartz crystals. Brown synthetic stones, resembling natural citrine, are obtained by adding iron to the hydro-thermal solution and by cutting the seed plate in a chosen direction. It seems that the brown colour is due either to ferric (Fe^{3+}) ions in the crystals, or to finely dispersed iron silicate present as fine particles within the quartz rather than in the crystal lattice [3]. Green stones are obtained by heating the brown ones in order to reduce the ferric ions to ferrous (Fe^{2+}), again present either within the quartz lattice or as finely dispersed particles. The violet colour characteristic of amethyst is obtained by using some radioactive source such as cobalt-60 to irradiate the crystals. This violet colour is produced by rather complex impurity centres in the material called **colour centres** [5]. These act as traps for electrons and it is the trapped electrons which are responsible for the selective absorption of light leading to the coloration. Fe^{3+} ions are thought to be required for the amethyst-type colour centre and their production demands a relatively high energy at a low temperature. This energy is most conveniently supplied by radioactive particles which bombard the material. If the bombardment occurred at high temperatures, the colour centres would not form because electrons could return to their original orbits, and indeed experiments have confirmed that the violet colour is destroyed if the stones are heated. The method used to produce synthetic amethyst probably duplicates that in nature, because natural quartz crystals can be irradiated over long periods by radioactive materials present in surrounding rocks.

The dark brown crystals of smoky quartz also owe their characteristic shade to colour centres. In natural stones these centres normally result from sodium (or lithium) and aluminium impurities simultaneously present in the crystals, which again must be irradiated. Colour in the synthetic stones is enhanced by adding small quantities of the element germanium to the solution and irradiating the resulting crystals, which are probably colourless prior to this irradiation.

Iron present in low concentration as trivalent Fe^{3+} (ferric) ions also produces yellow crystals. Very large yellow crystals have been grown by Sawyer Research Products. The blue stones which attracted Basil Anderson's attention at the Gem Testing Laboratory are obtained by heating cobalt-containing stones in a reducing (oxygen-deficient) atmosphere to convert the Co^{3+} ions to the Co^{2+} (cobaltous) form.

Coloured quartz crystals are not likely to be widely marketed, because of the low price of the natural stones. Attractive citrines, amethysts and so on can be obtained as cut and polished stones for less than £1 or $2. Coloured varieties of synthetic quartz do, however, provide a valuable addition to the range of materials available to the lapidarist and some very pleasing gemstones may be produced from them. At present the only material readily available is the pale blue or blue-green variety, originating in the Soviet Union, which sells (at about 10¢ per carat) in the form of pieces weighing 100–150 carats.

Table 6.1 Colours of Synthetic Quartz [3, 4]

Colour	Variety	Method of Production
Blue	(No natural stone)	Add cobalt and reduce by heating
Brown	Citrine	Add iron
Dark Brown	Smoky	Add aluminium and irradiate
Green	(No natural stone)	Add iron and reduce by heating
Violet	Amethyst	Add iron and then irradiate
Yellow	Citrine	Add iron
Yellow-green	Resembles peridot or chrysoberyl	Gamma irradiation + heat treatment [5]

OPAL

Opals differ from quartz gemstones in two major respects: they are non-crystalline and they contain an appreciable concentration of water chemically bonded to the silica. Of the four types of gem opal, the most valuable is black opal, which is normally a very dark blue with flashes of many other colours. The colour effects in white opal are similar but the background is white and milky, or a pale colour, while water opal has a colourless water-white background. The orange-coloured fire opal is transparent and differs from the other varieties of opal in that it does not show their characteristic play of colours. However it is structurally similar to them and not to single crystal quartz or microcrystalline varieties such as agate.

A decade or so ago it was generally considered impossible to synthesise opal. The formation of natural stones was believed to require periods perhaps as long as 100,000 years, and there seemed to be no way of compressing this process into a time-scale acceptable in the laboratory or production plant. The synthesis of opal has now been made possible only by an intensive scientific study of the structure and properties of the natural stones. Interest was particularly strong in Australia, where the world's most important opal deposits are found.

The first thing to be explained about opal is the origin of the unique and vivid coloration seen in the precious variety. The colours of opal are generally **pure**, which means that the wavelength of light coming from a small region of the stone occupies only a very narrow range of the spectrum. In this respect they resemble the colours of the rainbow rather than those of a painted surface or of other gemstones, which are a mixture of light of different wavelengths. The colours of opal can range from bright yellow and yellow-green, green, orange and red to blue and violet.

The coloration of opals is associated with small grains, ranging in diameter from less than a millimeter to several millimeters. Each grain has its characteristic colour, which may be the same as that of a neighbouring grain but is often different. It is a well-known observation that no two opals are exactly alike, and their differences may result from variation in grain size distribution as well as from grain colour. More significant is the observation that the colour of each grain changes when the opal is moved in such a way as to reflect light at different angles. This change in appearance is part of the charm of opals, but it is also an important clue in the search for the origin of their coloration.

Until recently the colour of opals was attributed to an interference effect, like the colours seen in soap films or in oil films floating on top of water. In these cases the colours arise because light is reflected from both the back and front surfaces of the films. At certain wavelengths there is an **interference** between rays of light taking these different paths and this eliminates reflected light at those particular wavelengths. It is a general principle that removing a particular colour from white light causes that light to take on the so-called complementary colour, and so thin films take on colours which depend on the thickness of the film and on the angle at which the light is reflected. Applying this idea to the case of opals, the theory was advanced that opals are made up of small spheres of silica which form films within a body of amorphous (glass-like) hydrated silica.

Detailed investigation of the structure of gem opals began in the early 1960's at the Commonwealth Scientific and Industrial Research Organisation in Australia [6]. The principal technique used has been transmission electron microscopy, which is similar to optical microscopy except that a beam of electrons is used in place of a beam of light. The great advantage of electron microscopy is that it is capable of very high magnifications, so that it can distinguish objects which are a hundred times smaller than can be resolved by an optical microscope. The main disadvantage of electron microscopy, apart from the high cost of instrumentation to accelerate and focus the electron beam and to produce the high vacuum in which the electrons must move, is that electrons have a very low penetrating power. The sample must therefore be extremely thin if all the electrons are not to be absorbed. To overcome this problem, the structure of opals was studied by making a replica of their surface in the form of a very thin film. First an opal was fractured in a vacuum to expose a clean surface, then this surface was bombarded with platinum at a very low angle. The platinum 'sticks' only at high spots on the surface and so it exaggerates the surface contours. Next the surface was bombarded with carbon to give a uniform film, and the platinum and the opal were both then dissolved in acid. This left a thin carbon layer which had the same contours as those of the surface on which it was deposited.

The electron microscope study revealed two main features, one expected and one completely new. The investigators were not surprised to find the silica present mainly as small spheres, typically 0.2 μm ($\frac{1}{5}$ micron or 2×10^{-7} metre) in diameter. What was unexpected was the observation that these silica spheres were stacked in regular geometric patterns, with holes in between each sphere. This arrangment immediately suggested an explanation for the colour of opals, because such a regular structure acts as a three-dimensional diffraction grating. **Diffraction gratings** are not in common use but are familiar to students of the physical sciences. The simplest form is made by drawing a series of very finely spaced lines on a glass slide. If a parallel beam of light falls on this grating, the colours of the

Fig. 6.3. Electron microscope photographs showing that opals are made up of tiny spheres of silica stacked in a regular arrangement.

spectrum are seen, often much more clearly than in the spectrum produced by a glass prism. The spectrum is produced by the inter-action of light scattered from a periodic array. An analogy may be found in the flow of water over rocks. A single rock sticking above the surface would disturb the wave flowing past it; if the waves were flowing past not one but a series of evenly-spaced rocks, the resulting disturbance could be expected to form a regular pattern on the water surface. This pattern would be related to the wavelength of the incident wave and to the distance between the rocks. Diffraction of light is similar but occurs on a much smaller scale, and definite wavelengths of light are diffracted only in characteristic directions so that single colours can be seen at certain angles from the grating.

Hence precious opal is now known to consist of transparent spherical particles of amorphous silica, roughly equal in size, which are tightly packed together in a regular array. Although the spheres are in good contact, there are spaces between them which are filled with air, water vapour or liquid water. The diameter of the spheres ranges from 0.15 to 0.3 μm in precious opals, and it is only this range of spheres which can produce diffraction colours over a wide range of the spectrum. Opals which are made up of silica spheres in a smaller or larger size range, or which have a wide range of sphere diameters, or poorly defined spheres, will not be capable of exhibiting diffraction colour effects. These are classified as 'common' as distinct from precious varieties. In fire opals, found mainly in Mexico, the spaces between the spherical particles are filled with material sharing the same optical properties so that diffraction does not occur. In other types of opal, irregular arrays of voids between the spheres cause a milky white appearance which is termed **opalescence***. The best black opals have very regular arrays of silica spheres containing iron or titanium, which absorb light and so darken the stone.

A detailed account of how such stones are formed in nature must be speculative, but the Australian group of P. J. Carragh, A. J. Gaskin and J. V. Sanders have advanced a general theory of the formation of precious opal [7]. The electron microscope studies showed that the spherical particles in opal are themselves built up from concentric shells of smaller silica particles 20 to 50 nanometers in diameter (2 to 5 $\times$ 10^{-8} m or 0.02–0.05 μm). These small particles form as

---

*There is some confusion between the use of the word 'opalescence' to mean the play of colours and also its use for the milky appearance which often accompanies these colours. The Oxford dictionary refers only to the latter meaning.

the water slowly evaporates and the concentration of silica in the
hydrothermal solution increases. In the formation of precious opal,
some mechanism must operate in which silica spheres of uniform
size are arranged in a regular array, often with hexagonal symmetry,
while spheres of different diameter are rejected as the opal gets
larger. The rejection of dissimilar spheres is likely to require a slow
growth rate, so the regions where precious opals are formed are
probably those where the water evaporates least rapidly from a silica-

Fig. 6.4. Electron micrograph showing the concentric shell structure of silica
spheres in precious opal.

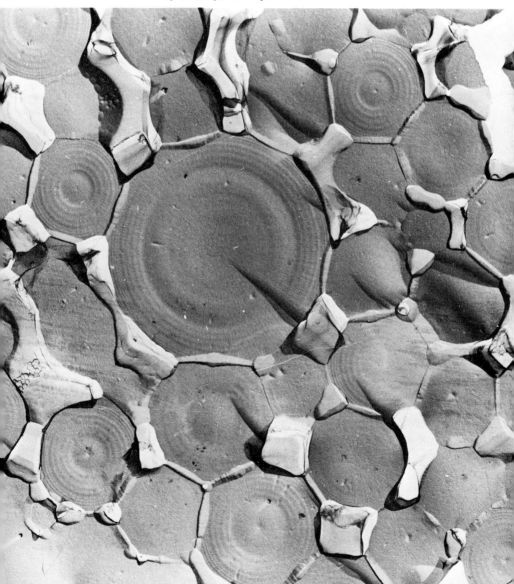

containing solution. Exactly what conditions in the Earth's crust give opal while others give crystalline quartz or amorphous silica are not yet known. However we may expect that the conditions will be rare in which large numbers of silica spheres of the correct diameter for precious opal will form. In view of the rarity of really high grade opals, it is especially unlikely that the optimum conditions for the regular packing of these spheres to form the precious variety will often be met.

Opals are therefore formed in nature under conditions where small spheres of silica settle together but do not grown to large sizes. The necessary requirements are met when a pure solution of silica remains in a cavity inside a rock formation with the water slowly evaporating, probably over some thousands of years. The deposit at Andamooka in South Australia has a layer of bentonite clay overlain by small boulders lying some 10 to 40 meters below a desert. The rock above the boulder layer contains silica, which could provide the source material for opal formation, and the bentonite clay below is impervious to moisture and so helps to isolate the silica solution. The opals are deposited in cavities between the boulders as the solution becomes concentrated by slow evaporation into the dry atmosphere above.

The gradual accumulation of knowledge regarding the structure of opal, and the resulting theory of its formation in nature, have made possible synthesis in the laboratory of this 'impossible' material. Techniques were already known for preparing fine spherical particles in a narrow band of sizes, and in this respect man has an advantage over nature because any natural solution of silica may be expected to contain a wide range of particle sizes owing to fluctuations in temperature during the precipitation process.

A patent for the formation of precious opals was filed in 1964 [8] by the Australians A. J. Gaskin and P. J. Darragh. The first stage of the process involves the preparation of a uniform set of silica spheres of the required size. A solution of sodium silicate is **deionised** by heating with ion-exchange resins for 30 to 300 hours at 100°C. This process precipitates **colloidal** silica spheres which then aggregate into the size range found in precious opal. Larger spheres which may form at the same time are removed at intervals by spinning the liquid and using a centrifuge effect. The resulting suspension of silica spheres is allowed to settle in a tall cylinder for a few weeks. As the spheres settle into layers, with the larger particles at the bottom, a pipette is lowered into the liquid. This withdraws a layer containing spheres of the same diameter, without disturbing the layers above or below.

The spheres prepared in this way are of hydrated silica, and the concentration of water molecules bonded to the silica is too high compared with that in opal. The conglomerate of silica spheres must therefore be partly dehydrated, either by prolonged heating at 100°C or by more rapid heating at about 600°C to cause the spheres to bond together. The patent also mentions the use of an adhesive such as polymethyl methacrylate. This impregnates the resulting solid, but without filling the air pores completely.

At about the same time as the early Australian work, R. K. Iler and G. W. Sears of Du Pont de Nemours & Co. of Wilmington, Delaware, USA, prepared silica particles 0.1 μm in diameter and observed brilliant colours in an intermediate layer between a dense, white, concentrated region at the bottom of the liquid and a dilute region above. When hydrochloric acid was added to the solution, they noted the formation of thin solid plates showing a range of colours from red, orange, yellow and green to blue and violet. This was probably the first reported laboratory duplication of the play of colours associated with opal [9]. The silica spheres were allowed to settle to form a conglomerate, which was then heated at 900°C to encourage them to bond together to form a rigid solid. Coloration effects were seen in the resulting material, but only when it was impregnated with a liquid such as water or butyl alcohol.

Later studies in Australia replaced the rather slow process using sodium silicate by a method using an organic compound of silicon, preferably tetraethyl orthosilicate [10]. This material is suspended as tiny droplets in a mixture of water and alcohol, and produces silica spheres of uniform diameter when ammonia is added to the stirred solution, precipitating them by a chemical reaction. The most difficult problem is how to consolidate the spheres to reduce the volume of voids between them and so improve the transparency. Impregnation with plastic leads to problems of non-uniform shrinkage as the plastic solidifies, and is undesirable because the resulting material must be considered an imitation rather than synthetic opal. The natural material could hardly be expected to contain plastic! It is therefore preferable to compact the spheres by heating, at temperatures between 500°C and 800°C. Crystalline silica is produced if the temperature is raised above 800°C, but opals of good strength and hardness have been prepared by heating at temperatures below this value.

In 1971/2 the first reports of opals prepared by Pierre Gilson in France appeared. The development of the process took four years of intensive research. The exact method which produces these gems is still unknown, but it probably uses either the tetraethyl silicate or a similar procedure to make the silica spheres, followed by heating to form solid opals. Only 5 to 6% of the raw material is reported to be used in opal production, presumably because this is the percentage which falls within the appropriate size range. The entire process requires a year. Both black and white opals have been produced, and these very attractive stones closely resemble the natural varieties. Gilson opals have been marketed since late 1973, and have remained the only true synthetic opals to be produced commercially.

The jewellery trade has been extremely active in its attempts to determine the characteristic features of Gilson opals and to evolve criteria by which they may be distinguished from natural stones. A detailed report [11] mentions that the white opals have a columnar structure when viewed from the side, and are pinkish-buff in colour with patches of pale pink, greenish-blue and yellow in transmitted light. There is said to be a 'dried leaves' appearance when discontinuities between grains are observed in a microscope, and the later black and white opals have a texture compared to 'lizard skin' or 'fish-scale'. Many Gilson opals are found to be porous and become transparent when immersed in chloroform. The porosity test seems to be one of the most reliable, but some natural opals also have a high porosity and will absorb liquids.

Of particular interest is a report [12] on Gilson opals by the Australian team who first revealed the structure of gem opal. They noted that the coloured regions exhibit patterns associated with columns about 1 mm in diameter which apparently form as the silica spheres settle during the sedimentation stage. These columnar patterns could, however, be modified by occasional gentle disturbance of the liquid during sedimentation and so may not always be usable as a distinguishing feature of synthetic opals.

The 'lizard-skin' effect described above is a sub-structure of the columnar grains and can be seen only under the microscope, whereas the grains themselves are visible to the eye. Again this effect could probably be eliminated by a small change in the manufacturing procedure.

When the electron microscope was used to examine Gilson stones they exhibited the same microstructure as natural opals, with very small spheres of silica packed into a regular array. However the tiny spheres in Gilson opals were not made up of even smaller spheres, as is the case in natural stones. In addition, Gilson opal contains a fine cementing material which fills the cavities between the spheres. Such a microstructure would not be expected to be highly porous, and it was in fact found that not all the synthetic stones were porous, at least on the outside.

SLOCUM STONE

In February 1976 an enthusiastic report [13] appeared about another man-made material which exhibits the attractive colour effects of opal: the 'Slocum stone'. Although the Slocum stone was called 'opal' in this report, it should be regarded as a substitute rather than a true synthetic because it is not composed of arrays of silica microspheres. Electron microscope examination by John Sanders [14] showed it to contain flakes of 'tinsel-like' material in a silica glass. It is non-porous and in this respect is 'a step beyond opal' (to quote from the promotional literature) because the porosity of natural or synthetic opals can be a disadvantage. A minority of natural stones develop small cracks after prolonged exposure to the atmosphere and serious cracking can occur if opals are immersed in warm, soapy water; if a ring is not removed before the dishes are washed, for example! It is the danger of this cracking which will no doubt lead Pierre Gilson to modify his process so as to avoid a high porosity in any of his new products.

The Slocum stone is not pure silica, nor silica plus water; the bands which give the colour effect are rich in alumina [14]. The glass also contains a little alumina, but with calcium and magnesium in such high concentration that the melting point of the stone is less than $900°C$ and therefore well below that of opal or quartz. The material seems to be made by alternating layers mainly of silica and alumina to form multi-layer films, and then heating to fuse a powdered glass matrix around it (or, strictly, to densify the material probably just below the melting point of the glass). However every carat was said [13] to require 20 gallons of water, which suggests a sedimentation process.

As in opal, the colours of the Slocum stone are caused by diffraction of light, their origin also resembling that of the colour of abalone shells, which are made up of fine layers. The jeweller will have no difficulty in distinguishing Slocum stone from opal, and the density of 2.41 to 2.50 is appreciably higher than that of opal.

The Slocum stone was apparently developed by John Slocum in a series of experiments between 1956 and 1964, and his work would possibly have taken a different direction if it had begun after the CSIRO electron microscope studies. The early research involved the rejection of tons of scrap silica, so much that the refuse collection service refused to handle it and it had to be dumped in an abandoned gravel pit. The early stones apparently had problems with cracking, but the material released in 1976 is said to be easy to cut or facet. Slocum stone is mainly produced for sale to lapidarists who will be pleased to have a material with opal-like colouring but which is easy to work. The stone is available in a wide range of background colours, the black being particularly attractive.

Cost is likely to be a very significant factor in determining the popularity of the various stones because natural opal can sell for over $2000 per carat. Gilson cabochons sell for $15 to $33 per carat for white opal and $95 to $154 for black, according to quality. Rough material for making triplets is available from only a little over $2 a carat. The Slocum stone, sold by MDI Corp of Royal Oak, Michigan,

Fig. 6.7. Electron micrograph of one of the films in Slocum stone.

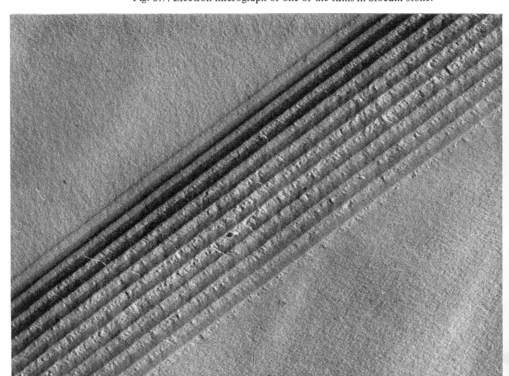

is a more versatile alternative for the lapidarist and should find its place alongside natural and synthetic opal. Gilson synthetic opal must be considered the most outstanding synthesis of a naturally occurring gemstone to appear in the 1970's.

REFERENCES

[1] B. W. Anderson, *J. Gemmology*, **11** (1969) 303.

[2] B. W. Anderson, *J. Gemmology*, **13** (1972) 1.

[3] M. I. Samoilovich, L. I. Tsinober and I. P. Khadzhi, *Soviet Physics – Doklady*, **14** (1969) 6.

[4] B. Sawyer, U.S. Patents 3,837,826 (Sept. 24, 1974) and 3,936,188 (Feb. 3, 1976); and private communication.

[5] D. R. Hutton, *J. Gemmology*, **14** (1974) 156; D. R. Hutton, *Physics Letters*, **12** (1964) 310; W. H. Dennen and A. M. Puckett, *Canadian Mineralogist*, **11** (1972) 448.

[6] J. V. Sanders, *Nature*, **204** (1964) 1151.

[7] P. J. Darragh, A. J. Gaskin & J. V. Sanders, *Scientific American*, **234** (1976) No. 4, p. 84.

[8] A. J. Gaskin & P. J. Darragh, Aust. Pat. 418,170 (filed Oct. 2, 1964); U.S. Pat. 3,497,367 (Feb. 24, 1970); Brit. Pat. 1,118,595.

[9] R. K. Iler, *Nature*, **207** (1965) 472.

[10] P. J. Darragh & J. L. Perdrix, *J. Gemmology*, **14** (1975) 215.

[11] E. A. Jobbins, P. M. Statham & K. Scarratt, *J. Gemmology*, **15** (1976) 66.

[12] P. J. Darragh, A. J. Gaskin and J. V. Sanders, *Australian Gemmologist*, **13** (1937) 110.

[13] M. Schowalter, *Lapidary Journal*, **30** (1976) 1370.

[14] P. J. Darragh and J. V. Sanders, *Australian Gemmologist*, **14** (1978).

CHAPTER 7

Other Synthetic Gemstones

Relatively few synthetic gemstones are produced on a significant scale other than those described in the previous Chapters. Where exceptions exist, it is normally because the supply of natural stones is becoming, or has already become, relatively scarce. Scarcity increases the value of a gemstone as it does any other commodity, and so it becomes increasingly attractive for manufacturers to synthesise a particular material even if the process presents difficulties of technique or of cost. Hence synthetic gemstones have a useful role to play (as was mentioned for the example of emerald) in supplementing the material naturally available so that more people can enjoy the beauty of a chosen gemstone, in synthetic form if not as the more expensive natural stone.

ALEXANDRITE

Alexandrite is a variety of the mineral chrysoberyl, a double oxide of beryllium and aluminium of chemical formula $BeAl_2O_4$. Chrysoberyl is therefore related to beryl ($Be_3Al_2Si_6O_{18}$) and especially to spinel ($MgAl_2O_4$) although it crystallises in the orthorhombic system and not in the cubic spinel structure. With a hardness of 8½, chrysoberyl is one of the hardest materials apart from diamond and spinel. The most common form of chrysoberyl is greenish-yellow in colour, due to iron impurity, and it was popular in the late 19th and early 20th centuries. Alexandrite is a rarer form in which some of the aluminium is replaced by chromium, and it occurs in Burma, Sri Lanka and especially in the Ural Mountains of the Soviet Union. It was named after Czar Alexander II of Russia, on whose birthday it was discovered in 1830.

The unusual colour change phenomenon known as the **alexandrite effect** is still not fully understood. In daylight, alexandrite normally appears grey-green or even deep green in colour, depending on the concentration of chromium, which in the case of naturally occurring material varies with the location of the mine. This green may have a slight reddish tint, according to how the light strikes the stone. However, once placed in artificial light, particularly that from fluorescent tubes, the stone seems to be red. Sometimes a change in colour can be observed just by turning the stone so that the light passes through it along different paths.

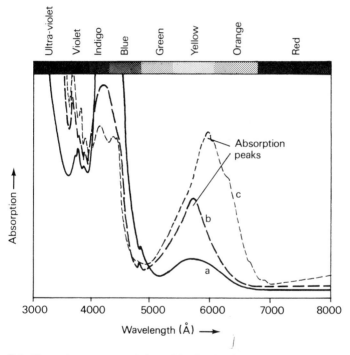

Fig. 7.1. Absorption spectrum of alexandrite for the three main crystal directions.

The alexandrite effect is related to the unusual role played by chromium ions within the crystal. Alexandrite is birefringent, and the colour change sometimes seen as the stone is moved can best be understood in terms of the difference in the absorption spectrum along different axes of the crystal [1]. The crystal system to which alexandrite belongs is orthorhombic, as stated above, and this means that the atoms are arranged in a rectangular array but with each side of the **unit cell** of different length. Blue light is strongly absorbed as it passes through the crystal in any direction. Along the so-called *a*-axis of the crystal, this is the only colour to be absorbed. Consequently, if alexandrite is viewed with the light passing only in this particular direction the complementary colour to blue is seen, namely yellow. Along the *b*-axis there is an additional broad absorption covering the red and yellow regions, so that the light transmitted is green. Yellow light is also absorbed if it travels along the *c*-axis, so that the crystal transmits both red and green wavelengths in this direction, with the red often dominating. Light reaching the eye after passing through an alexandrite is normally a mixture of many different wavelengths and is made up of beams which have traversed the crystal in a variety of directions with respect to the *a, b* and *c* axes. The eye integrates these various components and sends a message to the brain in which the alexandrite seems just one colour. As the alexandrite is moved, or as the conditions of illumination are changed, there will be changes in the various wavelength components of the light reaching the eye, and small changes may be sufficient for the apparent colour of the stone to change. Sometimes these changes in the wavelength components are so small that they are almost undetectable by a spectrometer, which measures the intensity of light at each wavelength rather than an integrated average. To this extent, the changes in the colour of alexandrite are partly physiological. That is, they are due to the nature of the human visual system rather than to any abrupt changes in the material itself. However, the relative strengths of the dominant red and green components in the light reaching the eye depend on the nature of the illumination. Artificial light is richer in the longer wavelengths, so that red becomes dominant. In daylight it is the green and yellow wavelengths, to which the eye is most sensitive, which normally dominate the colour of the stone.

Attempts have been made to understand the underlying causes of alexandrite's complex absorption spectrum. It has been proposed that the chromium (Cr^{3+}) ions are located on two different types of crystal site, one slightly larger than the other [2]. The alexandrite effect is also observed in a number of other gemstones, including synthetics made as alternatives to alexandrite.

Because the supply of alexandrite has been relatively low for some years, the marketing of synthetic materials has come as no surprise. A variety of vanadium-doped corundum has been available which exhibits an attractive colour change effect, but this is from a purplish-blue to pink rather than from green to red. The pink colour dominates and becomes stronger in artificial light, while the purple appears strongest in daylight. Synthetic gemstones such as this are not marketed only in technologically advanced countries but may find their way to the Far East. Many travellers have discovered to their cost that the 'bargain' alexandrites or rubies bought in Sri Lanka or Thailand were produced in a factory in Switzerland rather than by Mother Nature! In addition to the corundum a variety of spinel is also made which shows a colour change from green to grey.

Flux-grown chrysoberyl and alexandrite crystals were produced as early as 1964 by E. F. Farrell and J. H. Fang of the Massachussetts Institute of Technology [3]. These crystals were grown by slowly cooling a solution in a lithium molybdate flux, but were only 3 mm or less in size and not of good crystallographic quality. Four years later W. A. Bonner and L. G. van Uitert of the Bell Laboratories grew crystals up to 4.4 cm in diameter from a complex flux of lead oxide, lead fluoride, silica and boric oxide, using a much slower cooling rate of 0.5°C per hour [4]. Normally cooling rates as slow as this are expected to produce fewer, larger crystals containing fewer inclusions.

Alexandrite is also reported [1] to have been prepared by the Verneuil flame-fusion method but the quality and appearance of crystals produced by this method have not been described. Crystals can be pulled from the melt [5] but the resulting stones are disappointing in comparison with natural ones and are not such convincing and attractive alternatives to them as those grown by the flux method.

Alexandrite crystals are now produced commercially by Creative Crystals of Danville, California, and sell for around $300 to $500 per carat. This is a high price for a synthetic stone and reflects the serious scarcity of good quality natural material. The best Siberian alexandrite can sell for $6,000 to $20,000 per carat. The synthetic alexandrite was introduced in 1972 and was reported [6] to resemble Russian alexandrite rather than that from Sri Lanka.

The founders of Creative Crystals, Carl Cline and David Patterson, took out a patent on the preparation of alexandrite [7], an unusual step. Such earlier gem producers as Carroll Chatham and Pierre Gilson never patented their processes but preferred to rely on secrecy, in addition to their ability to produce superior material. The value of a patent in the field of synthetic gemstones mainly depends on whether it can be enforced.

The Creative Crystals patent reports that experiments were necessary to establish the optimum concentration of chromium needing to be added to chrysoberyl for the best colour effect. They found that iron and chromium together were necessary, rather than chromium alone. The iron to chromium ratio has to be adjusted according to the size of the gem required, another way in which man can make improvements over nature.

The normal method of producing alexandrite described in the patent involves the slow cooling of a solution of BeO and Al_2O_3 in a Li_2O + MoO_3 flux from 1200°C at 1°C/hr. The beryllia and alumina make up about 4% by weight of the melt, and the iron oxide Fe_2O_3 and chromic oxide Cr_2O_3 about 1%. The iron concentration is actually varied from 0.7% to 2.8% and the chromium from .001% to 0.5%. Seed crystals of natural or synthetic chrysoberyl are mounted on a platinum frame and lowered into the melt before the cooling begins. As many as 236 seeds are used, in two rows of 118 in a horizontal array. Growth takes 7 to 9 weeks, then the crystals are cut to remove the alexandrite from the seeds. The patent also mentions growth by pulling from the melt, which has given 400-carat crystals 3 inches long and ¾ inch in diameter. It is the flux-grown crystals, however, which are the most attractive synthetic alexandrites.

David Patterson, President of Creative Crystals, has sought to draw a distinction between cheaper synthetic gemstones, such as those produced by flame fusion, and the flux-grown stones which he calls 'created' – a term which the jewellery trade wishes to eliminate! Apart from their colour effect, the features which make flux-grown synthetics more like natural stones are the flux inclusions. The stones from Created Crystals contain wisp-like bubbles in undulating patterns, together with some coarser flux inclusions and triangular-shaped metal inclusions.

The price of flux-grown alexandrite is such that it is normally used in expensive settings, and it shows its best effects in a diamond mounting. If alexandrite remains a fashionable stone, we may soon reach the situation where the supply of man-made stones exceeds that of natural ones.

CORAL

Coral is unique among synthetic gemstones in that the natural material is of animal origin. It begins life as the framework of the coral polyp, a small creature about $\frac{1}{15}$ inch in diameter which inhabits warm seas and lives in colonies. Minerals are absorbed from the sea by the polyp and form part of its skeletal tissue. When the coral polyp dies, its skeleton remains in place and so a hollow tube of coral is left lying on top of the previous skeletons. In this way, over hundreds of years, very large coral reefs can be built up. The coral often forms branching structures.

Fig. 7.2. Micrograph of coral showing the skeleton of the polyp.

Coral consists mainly of calcium carbonate (calcite) together with a little magnesium carbonate and smaller amounts of other minerals, notably iron oxide. It is probably the iron oxide which is responsible for 'Corallum rubrum', whose dark red is the most highly prized colour, together with the paler rose-red 'corallum nobile'.

In Roman times coral was valued more highly than pearls, and Italy has remained the main centre for coral diving and manufacture. Coral is rather soft, having a hardness less than 4, and it is normally made into beads and drilled to make necklaces. Because of its softness and rather porous structure, coral will not take high polish but normally has a rather dull outer surface.

Coral has been dived for in the Mediterranean for so long that the relatively accessible sources have been exhausted, and divers must increasingly seek it at depths which are dangerous with simple scuba equipment. As harvesting the coral beds becomes more difficult, prices tend to rise, but it was still something of a surprise when Pierre Gilson announced the production of synthetic coral in 1976. This is probably the latest natural gemstone to be duplicated. The laboratory-made coral is said to use natural calcite from a French mine and to involve very high pressure and moderate temperature. In principle it should be possible to compress the powdered constituents of coral and heat the solid samples, probably in bead-shaped form, to cause densification by a process which is called **sintering** and involves the diffusion of ions in the material over several hours. This type of process has been used to make lapis lazuli simulants and is perhaps the method used by Gilson.

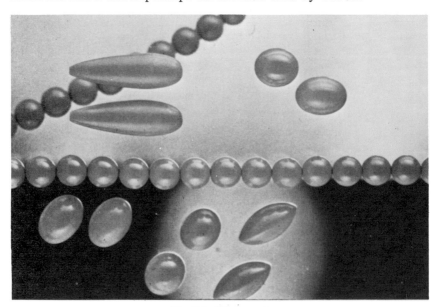

Fig. 7.3. Gilson coral.

Rough coral is available in various shades of red and pink, together with pale yellow and white, at a price of $135 per kilo for first quality 'rough'. Round, oval and pear-shaped cabochons are supplied in sizes from 0.75 to 32 carats, the cost of a bead varying from 42 cents to $6.05. It is not clear whether the Gilson coral should be considered a true synthetic because, apart from the impossibility of reproducing the polyp structure in the laboratory, there is some

Fig. 7.4. A comparison of the microstructure of (a) Gilson coral, (b) natural coral, at the same magnification.

doubt whether the colouring matter in the synthetic material is the same as that in the natural stones. The detailed compositions are also likely to differ, because natural coral contains a small amount of organic material while the Gilson literature does not mention magnesium carbonate, although this could easily be included. These details of composition will lead to differences in properties which may be used to distinguish the natural from the synthetic material.

Gilson coral costs about 1/5th the price of natural material of comparable quality. Whether or not the synthetic material differs in composition from the products of the coral polyp, lapidarists will welcome this attractive addition to the range of available materials. In deciding to produce synthetic coral, Pierre Gilson was influenced by Jacques-Yves Cousteau and the divers of the ship 'Calypso', who wished to persuade people to refrain from damaging Nature.

LAPIS LAZULI

Lapis lazuli is a beautiful opaque stone, found in quantity only in Afghanistan. Its attractiveness is due entirely to its colour, which at its best is a magnificent dark blue. Its name is derived from the Arabic word for the sky, al-lazward, used generally for anything blue. Lapis lazuli often contains traces of iron pyrites, 'fool's gold', which appears as gold specks against the blue background.

Lapis is exceptional among gemstones (though not unique) in

Fig. 7.5. Lapis lazuli made by Pierre Gilson.

that it is a polycrystalline granular material, and especially because it is a mixture of several minerals. Most prominent is hauyne, a complex mineral of formula $(Na,Ca)_{4-8}(S_3,SO_2)_{1-2}(Al_6Si_6O_{24})$, named after the famous mineralogist the Abbé Hauy. The minerals associated with hauyne in lapis lazuli are also complex aluminosilicates, nosean, $Na_8(SO_4)$ $(Al_6Si_6O_{24})$ and sodalite, $Na_8Cl_2(Al_6Si_6O_{24})$.

The mines in the Badakshan district of Afghanistan have been worked for over 6,000 years and have provided material which may be seen in a variety of historical locations throughout the Middle East. Powdered, the material was also used before the early 19th century as the pigment ultramarine, the blue colour used by the Old Masters. The blue coloration is associated with the sulphur, specifically with the electrons which are contributed to lapis by pairs of sulphur atoms [8].

Lapis lazuli has a hardness of only 5½ and is used in jewellery in the cabochon cut or as flat, polished plates. It is simulated by other naturally occurring minerals, particularly 'German lapis' or 'Swiss lapis', which is actually a form of jasper stained blue but lacking the gold specks of pyrites. Since 1954 a synthetic material imitating lapis has been produced by Degussa of Hamburg, using polycrystalline spinel doped with cobalt to give a blue colour. Specks of brass or even gold may be introduced to simulate the effect of the pyrites. More recently there have been other imitations of lapis lazuli, and late in 1974 an article by Robert Crowningshield [9] referred to four different varieties. Most interesting is the synthetic lapis produced by Pierre Gilson. This is said [10] not to contain any adhesive and to consist mainly of lazurite, which is a mixture of hauyne and sodalite. The synthetic lapis is found to be more porous than the natural material, but it has a superb colour, with or without finely distributed pyrites. However it is questionable whether even this material should be considered a true synthetic, because its density and detailed composition are not identical to the natural substance. Andersen's detailed examination of Gilson lapis [11] found some small differences from the natural stone, notably that the inclusions were softer than pyrites and did not have a cubic crystal shape. White inclusions were observed, not typical of natural lapis, and X-ray analysis showed traces of quartz and calcite, with a little iron. The material is said to take three months to produce, although a growth process as slow as that required for emerald is not necessary for polycrystalline gemstones. Rough material sells for $90 to

$250 per kg, while polished stones are available for about $8 per carat.

TURQUOISE

Like lapis lazuli, turquoise is a gemstone which has been known since antiquity and which owes its beauty to its magnificent colour. The stone was used extensively in Mesopotamia and Egypt but it was the Turks who introduced it to the French, so the name is derived from the French 'Turquois' (Turkish). Also like lapis, it is a polycrystalline material and is opaque to light. Chemically, turquoise is a hydrated copper aluminium phosphate of formula $CuAl_6(PO_4)_4(OH)_8.5H_2O$, with some aluminium replaced by iron. The colour is mainly due to the copper, although it may be influenced by the presence of iron, which gives a slight green shade to the dominant sky-blue.

Although it is made up of an assembly of tiny crystals, turquoise is slightly porous and absorbs moisisture when immersed. Its hardness is just less than 6 and it is not normally facetted but is incorporated into jewellery as regular or irregular polished stones of rounded shape. The finest material is used in beads or in the cabochon cut. The main sources of natural turquoise are Iran and the Western USA, where it is extensively used in jewellery by the Navajo and other Indian tribes.

As mentioned in the first Chapter, turquoise was one of the first gemstones to be imitated. In modern times a number of different imitations have been produced, using glass, plastic and even powdered natural turquoise pressed together and bonded with some adhesive. A true synthetic did not appear until 1972, when Pierre Gilson began the manufacture of his synthetic turquoise. As with lapis lazuli, it is difficult to understand why M. Gilson introduced this material. Natural turquoise is fairly plentiful, although the highest quality material is scarce. Unlike alexandrite turquoise cannot command very high prices, so the chief motivation for its synthesis is not likely to be for commercial gain. My own view is that Gilson produced turquoise in response to a challenge (because it was there!), to demonstrate his unique ability to produce a wide variety of very different synthetics – turquoise, coral and lapis lazuli in addition to emerald, ruby and opal.

The first synthetic turquoise to be examined in detail, by Robert Webster [12], was similar in colour to American turquoise rather than to the more highly valued Iranian material. Observation in a microscope revealed a granular structure which could be readily distinguished from the natural material, and which showed blue particles on a whitish background. The Gilson material was said, however, to be of very pleasing appearance and to take a high degree of polish. Since this report there have been a number of other studies of Gilson turquoise in the USA and Britain. In general opaque gemstones are rather more difficult than transparent ones for the gem testing laboratories, who must try to devise criteria so that the natural can be distinguished from the synthetic stones. Their problem is severe in the case of lapis lazuli because the variability in the natural material means that such properties as its density may vary rather widely. Differentiation between natural and synthetic gemstones will be discussed in more detail in the final Chapter.

Webster mentioned an early attempt at turquoise synthesis by M. K. Hoffman [13]. In 1927 Hoffman heated finely ground aluminium sulphate with sodium phosphate and apparently achieved some success, and it is possible that the same starting materials are used by Pierre Gilson. A report by Kurt Nassau [14] suggested that Gilson turquoise should be considered a true synthetic, even though examination in the microscope showed a mottled structure not seen in the natural material The compositions of Gilson and natural turquoise were found by electron microprobe analysis to be similar, as were the structures as revealed by X-ray diffraction. The refractive index for natural turquoise is 1.61 to 1.65, and for Gilson turquoise the specific gravity is 2.68 to 2.75, which is well within the range of 2.6 to 2.9 for the natural stone.

Gilson rough turquoise is sold at $135 to $750 per kg according to quality, in a medium blue ('Cleopatra') and an intense blue ('Farah'). Polished beads retail at around $8 per carat, roughly ¹/₅th the price of the highest quality natural turquoise. Gilson claims to have discovered the method by which turquoise is produced in nature, so that his material is a true synthetic although more pure than the natural stone.

REFERENCES

[1] G. J. Troup, *Australian Gemmologist*, **10** (1969) (No. 5) p. 9.

[2] F. Hassan & A. El-Rakhary, *American Mineralogist*, **59** (1974) 159.

[3] E. F. Farrell & J. H. Fang, *J. American Ceramic Society*, **47** (1964) 274.

[4] W. A. Bonner & L. G. van Uitert, U.S. Pat. 3,370,963 (1968).

[5] The possibility of pulling alexandrite from the melt is mentioned in [7] but without technical details.

[6] R. T. Liddicoat, *Gems & Gemology*, **14** (1972/3) 102.

[7] C. F. Cline & D. A. Patterson, U.S. Patent 3,912,521 (October 14, 1975).

[8] K. Nassau, *Gems & Gemology*, **15** (1975) 2.

[9] R. Crowningshield, *Gems & Gemology*, **14** (1974) 327.

[10] A. E. Farn, *J. Gemmology*, **15** (1976) 127.

[11] H. Andersen, *Lapidary Journal*, **30** (1976) 412.

[12] R. Webster, *J. Gemmology*, **13** (1973) 157; *Lapidary Journal*, **29** (1975) 1412 and 1428.

[13] M. K. Hoffman, *Fortschritte der Mineralogie*, **12**, No. 45 (1927).

[14] K. Nassau, *Lapidary Journal*, **31** (1977) 18.

CHAPTER 8

Synthetics of the Future

What new gemstones are we likely to see over the next few years? All the synthetic gemstones described in this book have originated in one of two ways: first there is the challenge to the experimenter of creating a material, originally produced by nature, which is both visually attractive and highly valued. This drive becomes stronger the rarer and the more expensive the natural stone. Then, entirely new gemstones have been produced as a by-product of scientific research into materials for specific applications, often in communications. Future synthetic gemstones will probably also arrive by one or other of these routes.

The question of what synthetics are most likely in the future has been considered in two previous articles, by T. H. Mariner of the Union Carbide Corporation and more recently by Michael O'Donohue of the British Museum. Mariner [1], in his 'Crystal Balling Future Synthetic Gemstones' (a title sure to horrify more conservative jewellers), considers those natural gemstones which have not yet been synthesised. He rules out such organic gemstones as pearl and ivory, which are produced by animals, and also rejects the cheaper minerals which are considered as gemstones, for example haematite. This is a black iron ore sometimes used for engraved stones. However he also eliminates lapis lazuli on account of its complex structure, perhaps rightly because the Gilson material may not be a true synthetic, as mentioned in the previous Chapter. Chalcedony, a variety of amorphous silica which includes onyx and agate, is unlikely to be synthesised on account of the natural stone's cheapness. The same being true, although less so, of spodumene, peridot, tourmaline and feldspar, Mariner's conclusions were generally negative.

Perhaps it is dangerous to conclude that man will never produce a true synthetic pearl in the laboratory. Pearl is mainly formed from calcium carbonate, not in the familiar calcite form but as a different structure called aragonite. The aragonite is in the form of thin plates held together by an organic adhesive called conchiolin, usually with a little trapped water. The pearl is formed by the oyster as it covers over any irritating object which intrudes into its shell. Whether man can find a way to achieve the same lustre as the best natural pearls looks doubtful at present but the achievement of synthetic opal should encourage caution in predicting what cannot be done.

O'Donoghue [2] mainly concentrates on the alternative source of new gemstones, and mentions a number of materials being investigated by scientists which might provide interesting new ones. Among those mentioned is bismuth germanium oxide ($Bi_{12}GeO_{20}$ and $Bi_4Ge_3O_{12}$) which are dense crystals bright yellow to orange in colour, of refracting index 2.55 and with a hardness of 4½. He also mentioned lithium tantalate, which is already available to lapidarists as mentioned in Chapter 5. Rare earth silicates in the apatite family, such as $NaLa_8Si_6O_{24}F_2$, are available in a very wide range of colours. La is the rare earth element lanthanum, and since there are 13 other members of this group of elements, each producing its characteristic colour, members of the apatite family display a remarkable variety. Another example of an unusual rare earth compound is provided by a bright green crystal of formula $Be_2CuPr_2Si_2O_{10}$ (Pr is the rare earth element praesodymium).

O'Donoghue's review also mentions some naturally-occurring minerals which have recently been synthesised, particularly by the hydrothermal method. Spodumene, a lithium aluminium silicate $LiAl(SiO_3)_2$, occurs in gem form as the lilac-pink variety kunzite and the emerald green variety hiddenite. V. A. Kuznetsov in the Soviet Union is reported to have made a green variety similar to hiddenite. Sodalite $Na_8Cl_2Al_6Si_6O_{24}$, a constituent of lapis lazuli, has also been prepared as dark blue crystals. Jun Ito of Chicago University, who grew the crystals of $Be_2CuPr_2SiO_{10}$, has prepared bright green crystals of nickel olivine, a solid solution of nickel and magnesium silicates of formula $(Ni,Mg)_2SiO_4$. E. Kostiner of the University of Connecticut also reported the synthesis of small crystals of azurite and malachite [3]. These are hydrated copper carbonates, respectively coloured blue and green, which occur separately or in combination as beautifully banded minerals. They are rather like agate in texture but with deep colours. Single crystals are extremely rare in nature. Finally, a bright green variety of phenakite, beryllium silicate Be_2SiO_4, doped with vanadium has been reported. This has a hardness of 7½, and large crystals have been prepared at the Bell Laboratories. All these stones are unlikely to be marketed except perhaps in small quantities for collectors.

NATURAL STONES

If the question of future synthetic gemstones is examined in more detail, it would seem that the next naturally-occurring stones to be synthesised will be those which are in such popular demand that steps are taken to supplement or replace a dwindling supply of natural material. The most popular gemstones are probably those which are listed as birthstones. Although this list may change from time to time, that recommended by the Jewellery Industry Council of the USA is listed below, together with synthetic alternatives currently available.

BIRTHSTONES

Month	Colour	Gemstones (Natural)	Synthetic
January	Dark red	Garnet	Red corundum
February	Purple	Amethyst	Purple corundum (or synthetic amethyst)
March	Pale blue	Aquamarine	Pale blue spinel
April	Colourless	Diamond	Colourless spinel (or YAG etc.)
May	Bright green	Emerald	Synthetic emerald or green spinel
June	Cream or green/red	Pearl	—
		Alexandrite	Doped corundum (or synthetic alexandrite)
July	Red	Ruby	Synthetic ruby
August	Pale green	Peridot	Pale green spinel
September	Deep blue	Sapphire	Synthetic sapphire
October	Variegated or pink	Opal	Synthetic opal
		Tourmaline	Pink corundum
November	Yellow	Topaz	Golden yellow corundum (or quartz)
December	Sky blue	Turquoise or	Synthetic turquoise
		Zircon	Sky blue spinel

The British list, recommended by the National Association of Goldsmiths, is similar except that alexandrite is not included as an alternative for April nor zircon for December. No mention is made in this list of synthetics, but cheaper naturally-occurring stones are included to cater for the less affluent purchaser: bloodstone instead of aquamarine, rock crystal instead of diamond, chrysoprase instead of emerald, moonstone in place of pearl, cornelian in place of ruby, sardonyx as alternative to peridot and lapis lazuli in place of sapphire.

Of the list of most popular gemstones, those not available in synthetic form are garnet, aquamarine, diamond, pearl, peridot, tourmaline, topaz and zircon. Synthetic diamond can be eliminated for the present on the grounds of its production cost, and also pearl because no way is yet known for reproducing synthetically the shiny outer layer. Of course, pearls are cultured by placing a seed inside an oyster, but these pearls are synthesised by the oyster and not by man. This leaves a 'short list' of six; aquamarine, garnet, peridot, topaz, tourmaline and zircon.

Aquamarine is a member of the beryl family, its fine pale greenish-blue being due to traces of iron. Unlike emerald, it is found in nature as very large single crystals, free from inclusions. Presumably it could be (and has been, see Reference [4]) grown from fluxed melts or hydrothermally using the same techniques as for emerald, but no reports of significant production have appeared. It may be that, although the finest quality aquamarines command high prices, the slow growth rate and consequent high production cost of beryls makes the manufacture of aquamarine unattractive on commercial grounds. The appearance of synthetic aquamarine on a significant scale is therefore likely to await a further increase in the price of the natural stones. An additional reason for the failure of synthetic aquamarine to appear is that the pale blue spinel used as an alternative is itself a very attractive stone and perhaps fulfils the requirements of purchasers seeking a handsome stone of aquamarine colour.

Garnets can be synthesised by the hydrothermal method and there is a patent [5], as well as several references in the mineralogical literature [6], describing the production of silicate garnets under high pressure conditions. Garnets were once very fashionable and commanded prices comparable with the more expensive stones. In the early part of this century they were more highly prized than, say, opal or alexandrite. At present the more common brownish-red garnets are relatively inexpensive, although it is possible that an attractive alternative could be marketed using suitable doping of

YAG or GGG. Manganese doping of GGG is said to produce a red stone, but whether the characteristic dark red of the natural can be reproduced in a synthetic aluminium or gallium garnet is not yet clear. Kurt Nassau's 1971 review of synthetic garnets [7] shows a wide variety of coloured YAG crystals grown by the flux method, but no traditional 'garnet' red.

Milan Kokta of Union Carbide has grown green uvarovite garnet by a flux method. Stuart Samuelson of Deltronic Crystals has also told me that he plans to market a true synthetic garnet in the near future, grown from the flux rather than hydrothermally. Since this information comes from a very experienced and able crystal grower, garnet must be high on our list of synthetics which are likely to appear on the market in the near future! However, the garnet he will produce is a green variety which is rarer and so more valuable than the red garnet.

Peridot is a member of the olivine family and is a magnesium iron silicate solid solution $(Mg, Fe)_2 SiO_4$, the iron, together with a trace of nickel, being responsible for the green colour. Although synthetic crystals have not been produced, the very similar material nickel olivine has been crystallized by the hydrothermal process [2]. The growth rate is likely to be higher than that of aquamarine, so peridot is one of the more promising candidates for synthesis in the late 1970's, although the natural material is at present rather inexpensive.

Topaz is one of the best known yellow gemstones, the most popular variety being a golden yellow. The name topaz, however, describes a whole mineral system and other colours are available; pale and brownish-yellow, blue, pale green and even rose pink. Chemically, topaz is a fluorosilicate of aluminium with some of the fluorine being replaced by hydroxyl OH^- ions, so that its formula is $Al_2(F, OH)_2SiO_4$. It crystallizes in the orthorhombic system and has been found, particularly in the Soviet Union, as some of the largest crystals produced in nature, though these do not have the prized yellow colour. Synthesis of topaz crystals is only possible by the hydro-thermal method, because the hydroxyl group would be removed on heating in a fluxed melt. Synthetic topaz has in fact been prepared, by the hydrothermal method [8]. So far, this synthetic topaz has been produced for research study but not for the gem trade. Clearly topaz can be synthesised commercially, but again the probability of its production will depend on the scarcity, and hence the price, of the natural stone. As in the case of aquamarine, an excellent synthetic corundum is available as an alternative to topaz, and the dark yellow variety of quartz obtained by heating amethyst, or produced synthetically, is also an acceptable replacement as a birthstone. This variety is often mis-named (illegally) 'topaz' or 'topaz quartz'.

Tourmaline is a very complex material with general formula $NaM_3Al_6B_3Si_6O_{27}(OH)$, where M may be magnesium, iron, or lithium and aluminium. In addition, other elements may be present such as chromium, vanadium and fluorine. Because of this complexity and variability, tourmaline can exist in an amazing variety of colours; black, colourless, pink, brown, green, blue and yellow, and various shades of these. More than any other gemstone, crystals may exhibit colour changes along the length or across the diameter, for example from pink to green. These changes reflect variations which occurred in the growing crystal's environment. Tourmaline is a rather common mineral, though not as the pink stone which is in greatest demand. At present, the supply of natural crystals appears to meet the demand, but again synthetic crystals have been produced by the hydrothermal method. The first growth of tourmaline on a natural seed crystal is credited to F. G. Smith [9] in 1949. A colour change

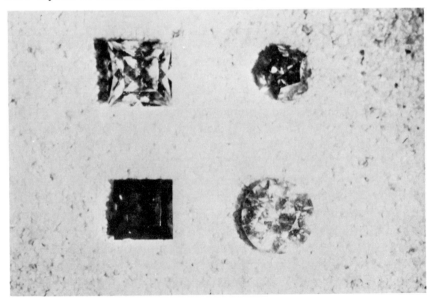

Fig. 8.1. Some new colours available in synthetic stones: YAG doped with neodymium (lilac); samarium gallium garnet (yellow); lithium niobate doped with neodymium (pale blue); yttrium aluminate doped with chromium (red).

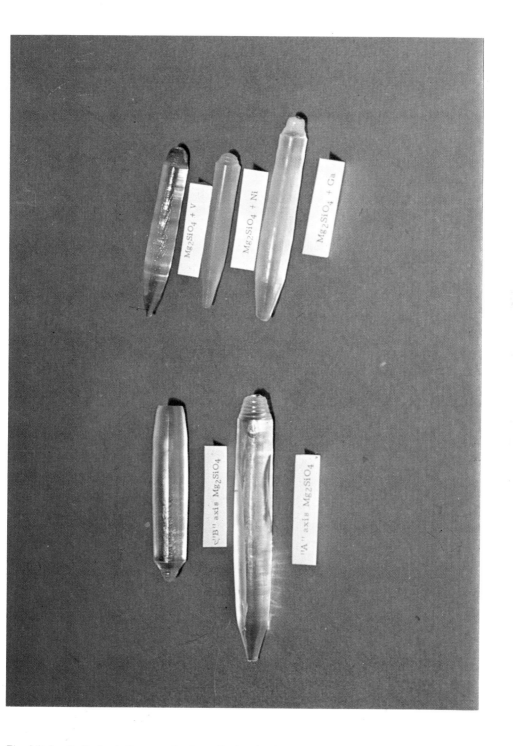

Fig. 8.2. Synthetic forsterite grown by Larry Rothrock of Union Carbide, including coloured stones.

Fig. 8.3. Neodymium gallium garnet with two samarium gallium garnets.

from pink to black was reported in the Soviet Union in 1960 [10] and a very extensive report was published by A. M. Taylor and B. C. Terrell in 1967 [11]. They replaced sodium partially by potassium or calcium and 'M' was magnesium, vanadium, chromium, manganese, iron, cobalt, nickel, copper or zinc. This wide range of substitutions makes possible an enormous range of colours, and so synthetic tourmaline could be marketed if the price of the natural material became high enough to justify synthesis.

Zircon has been mentioned earlier, in connection with its role as an alternative to diamond. The birthstone is a pale blue variety which is produced by heating reddish-brown crystals in a reducing atmosphere. The high refractive index and dispersion of zircon make its appearance outstanding, but it has never been counted among the 'precious' stones, partly because of its strong birefringence and brittleness but mainly because of public taste. Exactly what type of centre or impurity is responsible for the blue colour is not clear but zircon is known to contain hafnium, barium and thorium together with the more familiar iron. Synthetic zircons have been made, by both the fluxed melt and hydrothermal methods, and there is no doubt that a blue synthetic could be made given a modest research effort.

In summary, all six birthstones which have been considered are silicates, and synthetic versions of all could be produced by the flux melt or by the hydrothermal method. In either case, the likelihood of commercial production depends upon the rate of supply and demand, and synthetic material will probably be marketed in cases where the natural material is dwindling. Garnet is clearly the most likely of the six to be produced in the near future, because at least one manufacturer has a declared interest in marketing the stone. Of the other five, I would personally like to see a blue zircon synthesised since it is a most attractive stone. However, this would be likely only if hydrothermal synthetic zircon is produced for the electronics industry.

Apart from garnet, the natural stone which is most likely to be synthesised and then marketed on a commercial scale is not among the list of birthstones above. This material is imperial jade. The term 'jade' is used to apply to two district minerals, nephrite and jadeite. Both have a tough, matted texture and are perhaps best known for the many intricate carvings which have been made from them, particularly from nephrite, and especially by the Chinese. It is the emerald-green variety of jadeite, known as imperial jade, which has been particularly prized and used in jewellery. The green colour is caused by the presence of chromium, replacing aluminium in the formula $NaAlSi_2O_6$. Jadeite has a hardness of 7, but is mainly used in the cabochon cut and given a fine polish. Imperial jade has traditionally been considered as the supreme gemstone by the Chinese, and is still highly valued in Chinese communities, for example in the United States, where it also enjoys a widespread general popularity. The finest quality imperial jade, mainly from Burma, is in relatively short supply and there will almost certainly be attempts to produce a high quality synthetic. A patent for 'jade' production was granted as early as 1951 [12] but the list of constituents quoted for the imperial variety was so extensive (lead oxide, flint, potash spar, kaolin, zinc oxide, nepheline syenite and copper oxide) that the product could be termed only an imitation and not a synthetic.

The major problem faced by would-be manufacturers of synthetic jade is the texture of the stone. Jadeite has a granular structure, with the dominant sodium aluminium silicate intermingled with calcium magnesium silicate (diopside) $CaMgSi_2O_6$. Many minerals have been used to simulate jade, for example the green variety of quartz called aventurine. Although glass and plastic imitations have been produced, a genuine synthetic is still awaited. The best-known imitation is made by Dr. Satoyasu Iimori of Tokyo, Japan, and sells at $26 per kilo for rough. Dr. Iimori believes that it would be impossible to synthesise a true jade, and the magnitude of the task should not be underestimated. A good synthetic having the true imperial jade colour could be expected to find a steady sale among tourists wandering through the colourful shops of Chinatown, San Francisco, in addition to the outlets normally available to the jewellery trade.

Another gemstone which is not on the list of birthstones but has attracted the attention of the gem producers is cat's-eye. In the most general sense the term 'cat's-eye' is used to describe an effect, **chatoyancy**, which can occur in a number of stones. Chatoyancy is related to asterism, but in this case the fine needle crystals located in a translucent host material are aligned in a single direction. If the stone is viewed at right angles to this direction, a band of light can be seen running across the bundle of needle crystals. The effect can also be caused by fibres, channels or tiny particles not of needle shape, so long as they form rows along one of the crystal axes of the host material. Cat's-eyes are always cabochon-cut because this shows the effect best. The true cat's-eye is a variety of chrysoberyl, like alexandrite, and contains a multitude of microscopic channels which run parallel to the crystal direction of lowest refractive index. It is in this stone that a broad band of light running across the curved stone can best be seen, resembling the pupil of a cat's eye. Cat's-eye chrysoberyl is a brownish-yellow and the highest quality natural stones come from the Minas Gerais area of Brazil.

Cat's-eye chrysoberyl has become rare and is quite popular, so that the finest stones can sell at several thousand dollars per carat. An attractive simulant 'Catseyte' has been manufactured by Belgard and Frank of New York. Catseyte is not a chrysoberyl but is made from rare-earth silicates compacted into a mass of linear, parallel fibres about 6 to 10 μm (thousands of a millimeter) in diameter. These are fused with a coloured matrix and given a transparent coating of lower refractive index. Catseyte is another example of modern technology's impact on the gem trade, in this case the development of fine parallel optical fibres for the communications industry. A 1 cm cube contains over five miles of fibres. Catseyte is available in honey yellow, blue and green, and stones 5–14 mm in diameter cost from \$5.25 to \$29.95. The chatoyancy effect, of course, also occurs in a number of inexpensive natural stones, diopside, fibrolite, quartz and tourmaline. The best known is perhaps the brown 'tiger's-eye' which is a type of quartz. At the time of writing, no true synthetic cat's-eye chrysoberyl has been marketed, but David Patterson of Creative Crystals has told me that his company intends to produce this material. In view of his success with alexandrite, it may be expected that the synthetic cat's-eye will be a high quality product, comparable in appearance with the best natural stones and costing perhaps $\frac{1}{10}$th the price.

NEW GEMS FROM THE SCIENTIFIC COMMUNITY

Crystals grown by the scientific community are mainly of no gemmological interest. Materials such as silicon are the backbone of the electronics industry, and these are black and opaque, so there is on the whole little interaction between the gemmological and crystal growth communities. Where exceptions occur, as in the case of YAG, they arise in cases where crystal growers produce transparent and normally colourless crystals for some specific application. These applications have been in two main areas; for use in optical devices such as lasers and electro-optical components, and as substrate wafers on which thin magnetic films may be deposited. Optical uses gave us YAG and lithium niobate, while the latter field produced high quality GGG.

Of the materials available for optical applications, one of the most promising for gem use is that mentioned in O'Donoghue's review, namely lithium tantalate $LiTaO_3$. In 1972 Crystal Technology Inc. marketed this to scientific users, and they claimed to be the first to produce clear, water-white crystals of high optical quality. This material was sold under the trade name of 'Tantalite'. Lithium tantalate has a high refractive index, 2.175, and a birefringence of only 0.006, which is $1/20$th of that of lithium niobate. Its dispersion has not been reported, but refractive index data supplied by Frank Halden of Crystal Technology indicate a value of 0.087, roughly double that of diamond. 'Tantalite' crystals are grown by pulling from the melt and, although it is relatively expensive when produced in small quantities, the price could be competitive if it were marketed widely. This may be unlikely, mainly because of the rather low hardness value. However, lithium tantalate is an interesting material for use in doublets as an alternative to strontium titanate. Small amounts of 'Tantalite' have already been sold to gemmologists.

Michael O'Donoghue's review mentions that olivines and another member of this family, forsterite Mg_2SiO_4, has been grown as clear crystals by the flame fusion method [13]. A tricone burner was used and the powder feed consisted of silica with a magnesium ammonium sulphate. Better quality crystals have been grown, using the method of pulling from the melt, by Larry Rothrock of Union Carbide [14]. Iron, gallium, lithium, nickel and vanadium were used as dopants, and the nickel and vanadium produced attractive green and blue materials respectively.

Alternative candidates from the optical materials field are 'banana' $Ba_2NaNb_3O_{15}$ (also mentioned in Chapter 5) which has a refractive index of 2.31, and potassium niobate $KNbO_3$, which has a refractive index very close to that of diamond. New materials appear very frequently, for example $Gd_{0.15}Y_{0.85}P_5O_{14}$, gadolinium yttrium phosphate, which caused interest at the first European conference on crystal growth held in Zurich in September 1976. Yttrium vanadate, YVO_4, is another material which has attracted considerable interest and which should give an attractive stone if facetted. It can be doped with various rare earth elements to produce a wide range of colours. It has the same crystal structure as zircon, with refractive indices 1.86 and 1.88, but a hardness of only 5½, which is too low for use in rings.

Magnesium gallate $MgGa_2O_4$ is a member of the spinel family and may replace GGG as a substrate material for the deposition of thin magnetic films of ferrites if these are used in place of garnets for some applications. Spinels in general have lower refractive indices than garnets but magnesium gallate may have superior optical properties to the more familiar spinel, magnesium aluminate. At present, the introduction of any new material seems unlikely because cubic stabilized zirconia is so effective a diamond replacement.

Unusual coloured stones may find a place, at least as collectors' items, and the garnet family is a rich source of novel materials in both subtle and intense colours, in addition to those produced by doping YAG and GGG. On a recent visit to Union Carbide's Electronic Materials Division in San Diego I was shown an attractive reddish-orange crystal of lanthanum indium gallium garnet ($La_3In_2Ga_3O_{12}$) doped with cerium and grown by Milan Kokta. Larry Rothrock and David Brandle were enthusiastic about samarium gallium garnet ($Sm_3Ga_5O_{12}$), with its refractive index of around 1.9 and its intense yellow colour, and also praised neodymium gallium garnet ($Nd_3Ga_5O_{12}$) which has a similar refractive index and a deep grape colour not unlike royal amethyst. Both these materials would look very attractive in a setting of colourless stones and could become popular if grown for the gem market.

New materials are being developed so rapidly that it is not possible to forecast with certainty what materials will next appear as candidates for the large diamond simulant market or as fashion-able coloured stones. In the light of previous experience it can be confidently predicted that the scientific community will continue to provide some exciting and stimulating materials for the jewellery of the future.

REFERENCES

[1] T. H. Mariner, *Gems & Gemology,* **14** (1973/4) 241.
[2] M. J. O'Donoghue, *J. Gemmology,* **15** (1976) 119.
[3] E. Kostiner, *Journal of Crystal Growth,* **26** (1974) 155.
[4] *Gems & Gemology,* **14** (1972–73) 111.

[5]   W. D. Wilson & H. B. Hall, U.S. Pat. 3,468,801 (Sept. 23, 1969).
[6]   See M. J. O'Donoghue, *Synthetic Gem Materials*, Worshipful Company of Goldsmiths, 1976, p. 111–114.
[7]   K. Nassau, *Lapidary J.*, **25** (1971) 100.
[8]   P. E. Rosenburg, *American Mineralogist*, **57** (1972) 169.
[9]   F. G. Smith, *Economic Geology*, **44** (1949) 186.
[10] E. N. Emelyanova and T. A. Zigareva, *Soviet Physics Crystallography*, **5** (1960) 910.
[11] A. M. Taylor and B. C. Terrell, *J. Crystal Growth*, **1** (1967) 238.
[12] H. J. Kahn, U.S. Pat. 2,536,061 (Jan. 2, 1951).
[13] T. J. Shankland, *American Ceramic Soc. Bulletin*, **46** (1967) 1160.
[14] L. R. Rothrock, J. B. Hassell and H. L. Landt, Paper presented at American Physical Society Meeting, Los Angeles, December 1972.

CHAPTER 9

The Value of Gemstones

Those not familiar with the history of gem synthesis might be surprised to find that natural stones have retained such high values. Is it not remarkable that a 30-carat ruby of the finest quality might fetch £250,000, whereas an apparently identical stone made by the flame fusion process can be bought for £2? The reason for this huge difference lies in just one of the attributes of gemstones listed in Chapter 1, rarity. The synthetic ruby can be reproduced *ad infinitum* in the laboratory or factory, but a natural stone of comparable size and freedom from inclusions is very rare. So an analogy may be drawn, though not an exact one, with the difference in value between an original work of art and a copy. Artists sit all the time in the Louvre copying the Mona Lisa but, of all the millions of Mona Lisas now in the world, only one was painted by Leonardo da Vinci.

One of the major drawbacks in this analogy is that synthetic ruby is identical in its principal constituents with the natural material. Therefore the man-made ruby has inevitably the same crystal structure, the same distances between its constituent atoms, and the same properties such as hardness, refractive index, thermal conductivity and so on. However, small differences in properties arise because the environment of a crystal growing in the ground is not the same as for one growing in the laboratory, and these differences are normally sufficiently marked to permit the distinction to be drawn, just as Brand X margarine can be told from butter. Principally natural crystals differ from synthetic in that they contain a greater variety and higher concentration of impurities. They are also more likely to contain inclusions of the solvent from which the crystals grew at high temperatures in the earth's crust. Occasionally the synthetic gemstones exhibit their own characteristic defects. These arise because their growth rate is relatively rapid, as in the case of the curved bands and gas bubbles which often characterise crystals grown by the flame-fusion process. In the example of ruby, even crystals grown by the flux method can be distinguished from natural ones because the latter exhibit much less fluorescence under ultra-violet radiation, due to the presence of impurities which inhibit the fluorescence.

In other examples, such as that of emerald, the difference in price between the synthetic and the natural stone is much less. Emeralds are much more difficult to crystallize than rubies, and could not be marketed economically at the low rates possible for flame-fusion grown crystals. The price of man-made emerald is typically $1/10$th that of an equivalent natural stone, and this value mainly represents the level which the market considers acceptable. Other 'difficult' materials, such as alexandrite and even flux-grown ruby, can also command prices which are substantial fractions of those charged for the natural stones.

Materials which are 'difficult' to crystallize might seem less vulnerable to possibly major fluctuations in market value than those which crystal growers have found more amenable. Paradoxically, however, the most dramatic plunges in gemstone prices this century occurred with the 'difficult' diamond and the 'impossible' pearl. The value of pearls collapsed when cultured pearls first made their appearance, as it seemed that their rarity must inevitably decline. However gemmologists developed an instrument, the endoscope, which can detect 'seeds' artificially inserted into oysters and which can therefore distinguish with complete reliability between cultivated pearls and those produced unaided by the oysters. Once confidence had been restored, the value of natural pearls reverted to its former levels.

A similar though more short-lived crisis occurred in the 1930's with the introduction of spinel as 'Jourado diamond', as mentioned in Chapter 2. It is relatively simple to distinguish spinel from diamond, and the gem testing laboratories, which had been set up originally to provide a service for testing pearls, were soon able to provide reassurance to jewellers, and hence to the public, that the apparent threat to the diamond was illusory.

Since then, the gem testing laboratories have grown in reputation and it is upon their expertise that the value of gemstones ultimately depends. Therefore we should examine the techniques used by these laboratories, and assess their effectiveness.

GEM TESTING

The principles of gem testing are discussed in several books, the best known in English being those by Anderson [1] and by Liddicoat [2]. The techniques used by gemmologists for routine testing are relatively simple, but are reinforced by a wealth of experience and the accumulation of data on natural and man-made gemstones.

The gemmologist is faced with five principal types of problem:
  (i) To distinguish between high quality and poor quality stones of the same natural material. This is generally the simplest task!
 (ii) To distinguish between different natural stones, for example between zircon and diamond.
(iii) To identify rare gemstones.
 (iv) To detect fraudulent substitutions or imitations, for example 'doublets' which imitate a more expensive stone.
  (v) To distinguish between natural and man-made varieties of the same gemstone. This last can be the most difficult problem faced by the testing laboratories, because the properties of the two types of stone may differ only by subtle variations.

The identification of a particular gem species relies upon measurement of its physical and optical properties, which are unique to that particular gem. To a first approximation, these properties are the same whether the material is man-made or dug out of the ground. In some cases, the small differences between at least one property of natural and synthetic stones may be sufficiently large to be detected, but normally the detection of a synthetic stone is based on the study of inclusions within the stone. This may require observation with a microscope, although a hand lens will usually suffice.

The gemmologist is limited in the techniques which he can apply to measure the properties of a particular stone. The most severe restriction is that a test must not damage the stone, although occasionally such tests as hardness may be applied to the back of a stone where it will not be visible. Further constraints apply if the stone is mounted in an item of jewellery such as a ring. Assuming that the stone can be removed from its setting, its hardness, density (specific gravity) and refractive index, including optical character and birefringence, are normally measured. Additional tests may include the study of characteristic defects, especially inclusions, observation through special filters and the observation of fluorescence.

STANDARD TESTING PROCEDURES

Hardness is one of the simplest measurements to make and requires only a set of tools, each tipped with minerals of known hardness. However this test damages the stone and should be one of the last to be applied in gem identification, especially since the stone could be broken by only a small scratch.

The density of gem material is defined as the mass per unit volume and therefore distinguishes materials which have a 'heavy' feel from relatively 'light' stones like emerald. Often density is expressed as a ratio of the weight of the material to the weight of an equal volume of water. This use of **specific gravity** is convenient because it is independent of whether measurements are made in metric units or the old Imperial units. The actual measurement of density requires a balance to measure both the weight of an individual stone and the weight of an equal volume of water. The latter measurement makes use of Archimedes' principle, which states that when an object is fully immersed in water, its apparent loss in weight is equal to the weight of water it displaces. This loss in weight on immersion in water is therefore used to calculate the specific gravity. An alternative and simpler procedure for measuring the density of a stone is to dilute a dense liquid such as Clerici's solution (a thallous formate/thallous malonate solution in water with a specific gravity of 4.2 to 4.3) until the stone is just suspended in the liquid. The specific gravity of the liquid may then be determined fairly easily.

Refractive index is measured by a refractometer, and several versions are available commercially for measurements on gemstones. The value of the refractive index appears on a scale as the boundary between a bright and a dark region. In the case of doubly refracting materials, this boundary is not sharp but there will be an area of intermediate brightness between the two regions.

The optical properties of a gem material are particularly important and additional tests are often performed to determine whether the material is doubly refracting and to measure the birefringence, the difference between the highest and lowest values of the refractive index. A polaroid plate mounted on the eyepiece of a refractometer is useful in measuring the birefringence because it enables the tester to read the refractive index for the ordinary and extraordinary rays of a doubly refracting material. It also helps in measuring the difference between the highest and lowest values of the refractive index as the crystal is rotated. The polariscope is an additional instrument which allows the optical character of gemstones to be examined. It consists simply of a pair of crossed polaroids. **Pleochroism**, the unequal absorption of the ordinary and extraordinary rays in a doubly refracting material, can be examined using a dichroscope. This instrument uses a strongly doubly refracting prism, made of calcite, to produce two polarised rays which will be of different colour on passing through a material which exhibits pleochroism.

Another 'prop' used by gemmologists is the 'Chelsea' or emerald filter, which was introduced as an aid in the identification of emeralds. Emeralds are unusual among green stones in that they absorb a portion of the yellow-green wavelengths from the spectrum of visible light and transmit a portion of deep red. Because the filter passes little green but is transparent to the red, emeralds appear red through the filter, unlike most other green stones which absorb red wavelengths. The filter is used for some other identification studies as well, and other filters for particular uses also exist.

A much more detailed investigation of the absorption of light of different wavelengths can be made with a hand spectroscope. The use of this instrument, as is the case with many techniques in gem identification, was pioneered by Basil W. Anderson. formerly of the Gem Testing Laboratory, Hatton Garden, London. The absorption of bands of light in certain wavelength regions is associated with those impurities in the gem which are responsible for its characteristic colour. Absorption spectra of well-known gemstones are given in books on gem testing.

Fluorescence is another property which helps the gemmologists in gem identification. The stone being tested is irradiated with ultra-violet light, and certain materials have the property of transforming this invisible radiation to visible light. The wavelengths of this visible radiation, and hence the colour of the stone under the ultra-violet lamps are normally of two wavelengths, a shorter wavelength of 2537 Å and a longer one of 3660 Å (1 Å = one hundred millionth of a centimeter).

In summary, the most important tools of the gemmologist are the balance for specific gravity determination, refractometer, polariscope, hand lens and/or microscope and spectroscope. The dichroscope, ultra-violet lamp and filters are standard equipment in gem testing laboratories, but hardness testing would be used only as a last resort.

IDENTIFICATION OF SYNTHETIC GEMSTONES

The whole range of procedures which a gemmologist might use to distinguish natural from synthetic stones cannot be condensed into one short chapter. However, an indication of the general strategy adopted follows, with a few examples. For a more detailed account of gem testing procedures, the reader is referred to one of the standard works on this subject. Less detailed descriptions of the subject of gem identification are also given in many of the general gem books which are listed in the Bibliography.

Examples of criteria which can be used to distinguish synthetic from natural gemstones have been given in previous chapters. For example, the problem of distinguishing diamond from the various man-made or natural alternatives can be relatively simple because a refractometer will show a refractive index difference. Again, in the case of doubly refracting stones such as zircon, a simple examination with a hand lens will show doubling of the back facets. However, in practice a refractive index measurement is not so simple as this because conventional refractometers do not extend to values of 2, so excluding diamond and its most important simulants. If the stone is reasonably accessible, the refractive index can be measured using a microscope by the method of 'real and apparent depth' [3]. Alternatively, new instruments are coming on the market which measure refractive index in the diamond region. Ceres Corporation is planning to market an instrument which uses the heat conductivity of diamond for testing. The very high absorption coefficient of cubic zirconia in the ultra-violet range [3] could also be used as a means of detecting this material. Still another new instrument, the 'Luster meter' which measures the reflection of light from a flat gem surface, has been introduced by W. W. Hannemann of Castro Valley, California [4]. These examples illustrate the trend for the development of completely new gem testing instruments.

As has been pointed out earlier, gemmologists face their most difficult problem in distinguishing between natural and synthetic stones of the same gem, because the properties are then the same. Although other clues may be important, the detection of man-made stones mainly depends on observations of inclusions.

Gemstones may contain solid, liquid or gas inclusions, which are formed because the stone grows under non-ideal conditions. Two common types of inclusions are the solvent or **mother liquor** from which the crystal grew and, particularly in the case of natural gems, small crystallites of other minerals which were formed at the same time as the stone (or earlier) and became trapped inside it. The inclusions can be highly specific and present a powerful means, not only of distinguishing natural from synthetic gemstones, but of identifying the region from which a given natural stone originated. The authority on inclusions in gemstones is Eduard Gubelin of Lucerne, whose book *Internal World of Gemstones* is the standard reference work on the use of inclusions for gem identification.

Natural ruby crystals may contain fine needles of rutile, while the highly prized rubies from the Mogok region of Burma exhibit 'silk', large masses of fine intersecting canals which scatter the light as it passes through the crystal. Rubies grown by the flame-fusion method may be easily distinguished because they have the curved lines and small gas bubbles which were mentioned by Verneuil. The bubbles, which contain hydrogen gas from the oxy-hydrogen flame, may be spherical in shape or have small tadpole-like tails.

The case of flux-grown rubies presents a more difficult problem because they do not exhibit these curved bands and gas bubbles but contain inclusions which are more similar to those in natural crystals. Chatham rubies may, however, be relatively easy to identify because they are grown on a light coloured natural corundum seed. If these stones are immersed in methyl iodide, it should be possible to observe the pale central region. In addition, the initial growth on the seed is accompanied by a high concentration of trapped solvent inclusions which radiate outwards like the solar corona. This pattern is characteristic of rather rapid initial growth of the ruby on the seed.

In addition to included mineral crystallites, which can sometimes be identified by their shape and colour, certain patterns of 'mother liquor' inclusions are believed to be characteristic of natural or flux-grown ruby. For example, the 'fingerprint' pattern was for many years held to be typical of natural rubies, though such patterns have now been found in synthetic stones. Characterization by inclusions is also hazardous because the producer can change his growth procedure and so alter completely the pattern of inclusions.

The number of articles on the identification of emerald is particularly extensive, and so detection of synthetic emerald is very well documented [5]. The refractive index of flux grown emeralds is rather lower than that of natural stones, 1.56 to 1.57 rather than 1.57 to 1.59, and the birefringence is also somewhat lower, below .005 rather than above. The specific gravity is 2.65 to 2.67, compared with 2.68 to 2.77 for natural emeralds. The fluorescence of synthetic stones, including hydrothermal, is· normally much stronger than that of natural stones, because of impurities in the natural stones which prevent fluorescence. As an example, Linde hydrothermal emerald fluoresces bright red under the short wavelength fluorescent radiation.

Certain Gilson emeralds have been observed not to fluoresce under ultra-violet radiation, which illustrates how the crystal grower can introduce changes to produce properties more closely resembling the natural stones. In the case of the Gilson stones, the addition of iron is believed to be responsible for the absence of fluorescence.

As in the case of ruby, inclusions are of great importance in distinguishing between natural and synthetic emeralds. The natural stones often contain 2- and 3-phase inclusions (for example vapour and liquid or vapour, liquid and solid together), and commonly have mineral inclusions such as mica, actinolite or pyrite crystallites. Flux-grown emeralds frequently have wispy inclusions of solidified flux, possibly together with gas bubbles. Phenakite crystallites may be present, as in hydrothermal emerald.

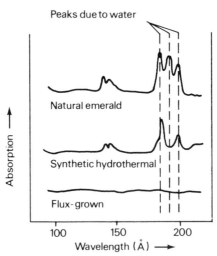

Fig. 9.1. Infra-red absorption spectra of emeralds, showing the. –OH absorption bands due to the presence of water in hydrothermal and natural stones.

In summary, diagnosis of flux-grown emerald is mainly on the basis of its red fluorescence, low specific gravity, low refractive index and birefringence, and 'veil' or 'feather' inclusion patterns. An infra-red absorption measurement is particularly significant in identifying flux-grown emeralds, because the absorption bands due to the presence of -OH groups from the water solvent are absent. However these bands are present in synthetic hydrothermal emerald. The infra-red spectrometer required for such measurements is, however, not generally available to jewellers.

This example shows how the gem testing laboratories have begun to require increasingly sophisticated instrumentation in recent years, to meet the challenges posed by new materials and by greater skill on the part of the producers in synthesising gems which exhibit more closely the properties of the natural material. The opaque, poly-crystalline gem materials present particularly difficult problems for testers. In part this results from the variability in the properties of the natural stones. For example, the specific gravity of natural turquoise can range between 2.3 and 2.8, due partly to variations in composition but mainly to porosity, the presence of tiny air pores between the grains of turquoise. Although the specific gravity of the synthetic material may vary, it will always fall within this broad range. Similar variations occur in other properties and there is at present no single criterion which gives a really reliable test for Gilson synthetic turquoise. Detailed tests of synthetic coral have yet to be reported.

The example of opal shows most clearly the value of applying modern instruments for materials characterization to solve problems in gemmology. Collaboration between gemmologists and scientists appears particularly strong in Australia. For example C. M. Scala of Monash University has reviewed research on the study of impurities in gems by electron spin resonance and other techniques [6].

The gem testing laboratories are responding to this challenge and the headquarters of the Gemmological Institute of America now has a scanning electron microscope with microprobe analyser. This instrument can examine gems at magnifications up to 150,000X and can also determine the chemical composition of the material, or of inclusions if these are exposed at the surface [7]. In addition, an automatic recording spectrophotometer measures the dependence on wavelength of a gem's absorption or reflection of light. This instrument can be combined with a research microscope to examine colour-related effects in small areas. The information can be stored in a computer, so that a body of readily-accessible information may be built up. This sort of approach is very desirable if the jewellery trade is to have confidence in the ability of its testing laboratories to provide accurate identification of gems.

GEMS AS INVESTMENTS

In recent years there has been a growing tendency for investors to buy gems as a hedge against inflation. Such investments are normally of a long-term nature because dealer mark-ups are higher than for many other investments and so considerable appreciation in the value of the stone is necessary just to pay the dealers' profits. The profit is presumably justified by the expertise necessary to guarantee the authenticity and value of the stone, because the investor must rely on a professional appraisal.

Rarity, durability, clarity, colour or fire and brilliance and size are the factors which will be most important in determining this appraisal, as mentioned previously. The laws of supply and demand must also be remembered, and those of fashion too: opals, now very popular, fell into disrepute in the 17th century because they were regarded as unlucky, a slur from which they have only recovered comparatively recently. Cubic zirconia at present has a novelty value which tends to make its price high. Although its production cost and relatively low yield will keep it more expensive than YAG, the price is expected to drop to around $15 per carat for cut stones, half the present price. The same trend can be expected with any innovation, as in the case of LED watches which now sell for $\frac{1}{10}$th of their original price. Well-established synthetics, like natural stones, tend to appreciate and scarce varieties can become collectors' items.

Hence we can conclude that synthetic gemstones can 'peacefully co-exist' with natural stones, the two complementing each other rather than competing. The examples of cultured pearls, 'Jourado diamonds' and real synthetic diamonds show that, once the initial shock has died down, the price of natural gemstones reverts to what it would have been in the absence of man's innovation. Of course this may not always be the case, but the gem trade has been highly stable so far and can be expected to continue to be so even in the presence of enterprising and skilful inventors and gem producers.

REFERENCES

[1] B. W. Anderson, *Gem Testing,* 8th Edition, Butterworth, 1971.
[2] R. T. Liddicoat, *Handbook of Gem Identification,* 6th Edition, Gemmological Institute of America, Los Angeles, 1972.
[3] G. Bosshart, *Lapidary Journal,* 31 (1977) 1954.

[4]　W. W. Hannemann, *Lapidary Journal,* 31 (1977) 846.
[5]　See, in particular, E. M. Flanigen, D. W. Breck, N. R. Mumbach and A. M. Taylor, *American Mineralogist,* 52 (1974) 119.
[6]　C. M. Scala, *Australian Gemmologist,* 17 (1974) 119.
[7]　Anon, *Lapidary Journal,* 31 (1978) 2352.

Appendix 1

PROPERTIES OF COMMON GEMSTONES

Gem	Formula	Crystal System	Hardness	Specific Gravity	Refractive Index	Refraction
Alexandrite	$BeAl_2O_4$	Rhombic	8½	3.72	1.74–1.75	Double
Aquamarine	$Be_3Al_2Si_6O_{18}$	Hexagonal	7½	2.70	1.57–1.58	Double
Diamond	C	Cubic	10	3.52	2.42	Single
Emerald	$Be_3Al_2Si_6O_{18}$	Hexagonal	7½	2.69	1.57–1.58	Double
Garnet (Demantoid)	$Ca_3Fe_2Si_3O_{12}$	Cubic	6½	3.84	1.88	Single
Garnet (Pyrope)	$Mg_3Al_2Si_3O_{12}$	Cubic	7¼	3.75	1.75	Single
Jade (jadeite)	$NaAlSi_2O_6$	Monoclinic	7	3.34	1.65–1.66	—
Kunzite	$LiAlSi_2O_6$	Monoclinic	6½	3.18	1.66–1.67	Double
Lapis-lazuli	Variable	Cubic	5½	2.85	1.50	—
Opal	$3SiO_2.H_2O$ (approx)	Amorphous	6	2.10	1.45	Single
Peridot	Mg_2SiO_4	Rhombic	7	3.33	1.65–1.69	Double
Quartz	SiO_2	Trigonal	7	2.65	1.54–1.55	Double
Ruby	Al_2O_3	Hexagonal	9	3.99	1.76–1.77	Double
Rutile	TiO_2	Tetragonal	6	4.25	2.62–2.90	Double
Sapphire	Al_2O_3	Hexagonal	9	3.99	1.76–1.77	Double
Spinel (natural)	$MgAl_2O_4$	Cubic	8	3.60	1.72	Single
Spinel (synthetic)	$MgAl_2O_{10-5}$	Cubic	8	3.63	1.73	Single
Strontium titanate	$SrTiO_3$	Cubic	6	5.13	2.41	Single
Topaz	$Al_2SiF_2O_4$	Rhombic	8	3.53	1.63–1.64	Double
Tourmaline	$Al_3H_{11}B_2Si_4O_{11}$	Trigonal	8	3.10	1.62–1.65	Double
Turquoise	$Al_2(OH)_3PO_4.H_2O$	Amorphous	6	2.75	1.60	—
Zircon	$ZrSiO_4$	Tetragonal	7½	4.1–4.8	1.81–1.98	Double

†See also Chapter 5, Table 5.1

Appendix 2

GLOSSARY OF SOME SPECIALISED TERMS

Amorphous. Having no regular arrangement of atoms into a crystal structure, so no cleavage or double refraction.

Asterism. The property of stones which show a star in reflected light.

Birefringence. The difference between the two refractive indices of doubly refracting materials.

Boule. Cylindrical shaped crystal grown by the flame fusion or other process.

Brilliance. The ability of gemstones to reflect light, related to its cut and to the refractive index of the material.

Cabochon. A way of polishing to give a rounded, non-facetted stone.

Carat. A unit of weight, ⅕th of a gram. Also used as a measure of the purity of gold, pure gold being 24 carat.

Complementary colour. The colour produced when light of a certain wavelength is removed from white light. For example, red and yellow-green are complementary so that red light may be produced by removing yellow-green light from white light.

Crown. The upper part of a cut gemstone.

Crystal (Single crystal). A solid in which the atoms are arranged in a characteristic unit which is repeated in three dimensions throughout the material.

Density. The ratio of the mass of a body to its volume.

Dimensions (Length). 1 μm (micron) = one thousandth of a mm or 0.04 mil. 1 Å (Angstrom unit) = 10^{-8} cm = one hundredth millionth of a cm.

Disperson. See 'Fire'.

Doping. The introduction of controlled quantities of 'impurities'.

Double refraction. A property of materials such that refracted light is split into two rays; the material therefore has two refractive indices.

Doublet. A composite stone in which the crown and pavilion are of different materials.

Facet. A flat polished surface of a cut gemstone. Also used for the flat surfaces which occur on natural or synthetic crystals.

Fire. Popular term for the dispersion of white light into the colours of the spectrum (rainbow).

Flame fusion. A method of growing crystals in which a fine powder melts on passing through a flame.

Flux. A high-temperature solvent used to grow synthetic gems by 'flux fusion'.

Fusion. Melting.

Gemstone. A stone valued because of its beauty.

Girdle. The widest part of a cut gemstone where the crown meets the pavilion.

Glass. A particular type of amorphous material in which the atomic arrangement of the liquid state is preserved.

Habit. The characteristic shape of a natural or synthetic crystal.

Hardness. The power of a gemstone to resist deformation. Hardness of gems is normally measured on the Mohs scale.

Hydrothermal. A term used to denote the growth of gemstones from a solution in water at high temperatures and pressures.

Imitation. These gemstones are similar to natural but differ in chemical composition, structure and so on.

Inclusions. Impurities trapped in a gemstone as particles normally visible to the eye or in a microscope.

Metastable. Describing a condition where a material has an indefinite lifetime although it is not the stable phase, for example glass at room temperature.

Nucleation. The initial formation of tiny crystals in some medium where crystal growth is to occur.

Pavilion. The lower part of a cut gemstone.

Phase. A separable condition of matter for example liquid, solid or vapour. Also applied to solids having different crystal structure, for example graphite and diamond are the crystalline solid phases of carbon.

Polycrystalline. Made up of many crystals.

Pressure. 1 atmosphere is about 14 lb per square inch; 1 torr $=$ the pressure exerted by a 1 mm height of mercury, or $\frac{1}{760}$ of an atmosphere.

Recrystallization. Heat treatment of polycrystalline materials to produce larger crystals. Also used to describe processes involving a liquid or vapour process of transforming crystals.

Refractive index. The ability of a material to bend light. Given by the ratio of the speed of light in a vacuum to that in the material.

Relative density. The ratio of the mass of a body to that of an equal volume of water. Numerically equal to the specific gravity.

Seed. A small crystal upon which a large crystal is grown.

Spectrum. The constituent colours of visible light, seen when white light is dispersed into its various wavelengths.

Synthetic. Strictly means built up from its constituent chemical elements (synthesised). Not to be confused with 'imitation'.

Table. The largest facet at the top of the crown of a cut gemstone.

Appendix 3

HOW TO GROW YOUR OWN RUBIES

Growing rubies by the flame fusion process in the garage is possible, but not recommended. Occasionally flame fusion furnaces become available cheaply as companies cease manufacture, so the actual cost of the apparatus can be low. However, the hydrogen and oxygen gases required are rather expensive, the price often varying according to the volume used and the location of the delivery point, and the small user cannot expect a bargain price. Also, the products of Djeva in particular are relatively cheap and readily available, though much less like natural rubies than those grown from fluxed melts. We will therefore consider flux growth of ruby.

Even this venture is not one which should be undertaken lightly. Although not exactly a hobby for millionaires, the capital outlay is considerable and the outcome of the experiments somewhat uncertain in the absence of previous experience (even with it!). The basic requirements are a crucible, furnace, temperature controller with thermocouple, and chemicals. The crucible must be of platinum and is likely to be the most difficult item to obtain. Because the price of platinum is lower to the scientific community than on the open market, the suppliers (Johnson Matthey Metals of 83 Hatton Garden, London EC1 or Baker Platinum (Englehard) in England and the USA) will wish to know the use to which the crucible will be put. A 250 ml crucible is the recommended size to start with, large enough to grow crystals of reasonable size but not disastrously expensive. The cost depends mainly on the weight of the crucible and so on the wall thickness. This will be in the region of $1000, but the crucible retains most of its value as scrap platinum so that only the fabrication and recovery costs are totally lost, and even these may be offset by inflation in the value of platinum. The crucible must have a tightly-fitting lid which will add perhaps 35% to the cost.

Furnaces to reach 1250°C or so can be obtained commercially from various laboratory suppliers, although most professional 'flux growers' build their own. Heating elements for the furnace will probably come from the Carborundum company although Morganite could be considered in Britain. Six to eight ½ inch diameter rods, each 18 to 24 inches in overall length and 6 inch in heating length are typical. The furnace is a very simple structure built from firebricks around a cavity about 9 inch cube. The heating element suppliers will provide drawings of suitable furnace designs and construction is facilitated because firebricks are very friable and so can be either cut with a hacksaw or drilled. It has been considered good practice to build the furnace inside an enclosure of a strong asbestos-containing compound. However, in view of the health hazards now known to be associated with asbestos dust, some alternative would now seem to be recommended. The absence of some other strong heat-insulator makes the purchase of a ready-assembled furnace look more attractive.

Furnace temperature controllers are available from many suppliers but the one chosen must give close control, certainly better than 1°C for good results. My own preference is for Eurotherm of Bognor Regis, Sussex, who have a network of agents in the USA. A 15 amp, 240V model should give adequate power (or 30 amp, 110V). These controllers have a limiter to regulate the maximum current supplied to the furnace, and matching programmers can also be obtained which allow the temperature of the furnace to be cooled at a con-trolled and stable rate. Cheaper ways of cooling the furnace are possible, by driving a helical potentiometer using a motor, but will not give such good performance.

Chemicals are fairly easy to obtain because there are a number of manufacturers, and it is more conveneient to get all those required from a local supplier who may handle chemicals from more than one major company. In general, chemicals of analytic reagent or similar grade are recommended because these are relatively inexpensive but have a lower impurity content than the cheapest grades. Professional flux growers normally use 'spectroscopic grade' chemicals and Grade II materials from Johnson Matthey Chemical Co., Royston, Herts are worth considering (but seem to be expensive outside the UK because of shipping and dealer handling charges). The chemicals required will be lead fluoride PbF_2 and lead oxide PbO (a specialist supplier is NL Industries of Amboy, New Jersey) boric oxide B_2O_3, aluminium oxide Al_2O_3 and chromic oxide Cr_2O_3. A small amount of lan-thanum oxide will improve the shape of the crystals. This is expensive and a relatively impure grade will suffice since it is used in low concentrations.

A variety of techniques can be used to grow the rubies, the most popular being flux evaporation, gradient transport and slow cooling. The idea of slowly increasing the concentration of ruby constituents in the melt by evaporation of the lead solvents is one which can also be applied very easily to solutions of various salts in water. However, in the case of lead salt solutions there is the important problem that lead compounds are poisonous, and the toxic effects are cumulative[†]. Although lead fluoride (the main constituent of the volatile species) condenses quickly as it cools on escape from the furnace, the toxicity problem is sufficiently serious to make some alternative seem preferable.

Gradient transport has produced good results and two references [1, 2] which describe the successful growth of large rubies are given at the end of the Section. This method has the disadvantage that it requires seed crystals, and so for initial experiments the use of slow cooling is advised.

The procedure suggested here loosely follows that outlined in the paper of Linares [3], who obtained the largest flux-grown rubies to have been described in the crystal growth literature. In a typical experiment, 12 grams of ruby (alumina with 1% or so of chromic oxide) are added to 50 grams of PbO with 50 grams of PbF_2. This mixture is heated to 1250°C over a few hours and held at this temperature for long enough to dissolve the alumina; this will also require several hours and 12 to 24 hours is recommended. Cooling of the furnace is then begun, at a rate of one degree per hour or less, until a temperature of 950°C is reached, when the power supply can be turned off and the crucible allowed to cool in the furnace.

The crystals are recovered from the solidified melt by leaving the crucible in a bath of dilute nitric acid. This process may take several days, although it can be speeded up by warming the acid, occasional agitation and frequent changing of the acid. This procedure requires an enclosure because the acid fumes must not be inhaled.

Many variations on the above procedure are possible. Increasing the weight of material used will give better results and the size of the charge should be progressively raised until the crucible is half to two-thirds full after melting. This may require several pre-melts of the powder since there is a considerable shrinkage on melting. Some of the lead oxide can be replaced by boric oxide B_2O_3, about 2 to 4 grams in 50 is considered optimum. The chromic oxide

†Great care must always be used in handling lead compounds.

concentration can be varied, a low concentration giving a pale stone and several % a deep red. Lanthanum oxide has a beneficial effect on the morphology of the crystals, giving a more rhombohedral and so less platey habit. A. B.. Chase [4] reported good results with 0.5% to 1% La_2O_3, about 1 to 2 g in the melt above. The melt in the original experiments contained 142 g lead fluoride, 102 g bismuth oxide Bi_2O_3, 20 g Al_2O_3 and up to 3 g La_2O_3.

The main problems which will be encountered in attempts to grow large ruby crystals are nucleation of too many crystals, the tendency of crystals to grow as platelets, non-uniform colour and flux inclusions. References [1 to 4] may be consulted for the experiences of some expert crystal growers. In addition two innovations which should be beneficial for the size and quality of crystals may be tried. Growing the crystals in the fastest possible time requires matching the furnace cooling rate to the size of the crystals, and slow cooling rates are particularly desirable in the early stages when crystals are small and so have little surface area on which the crystallizing ruby can deposit. 'Programmed growth' using varying cooling rates has been discussed in a detailed paper [5] but experiments involving non-linear cooling are really effective only if the temperature of nucleation is accurately known. In the absence of knowledge of the temperature where crystals start to form, a constant cooling rate is a reasonable alternative.

The problems of crystal growth can be reduced by stirring the melt both before and during growth using the accelerated crucible rotation technique [6, 7]. Stirring makes the solution homogeneous and so reduces nucleation, in addition to increasing the maximum rate at which crystal can be grown. The growth of rubies from stirred solutions has not yet been reported in the crystal growth literature, so the first person to try this technique would be performing original research. Two requirements must be met before this technique can be applied successfully: sealing of the crucible lid to slow down the rate of evaporation of the lead fluoride, and local cooling of the centre of the crucible base to provide a spot where the crystals can nucleate and grow. A ½ inch hole in the ceramic support used to hold the crucible, so that there is preferential radiation from the central zone, is the simplest means of providing a cool spot and should be effective. The platinum lid is normally sealed by welding using an oxy-acetylene torch with a fine nozzle. Many techniques used in crystal growth by the flux method have been described in a comprehensive monograph on this subject [7].

REFERENCES

[1] E. A. D. White and J. W. Brightwell, *Chemistry and Industry,* (1965) 1662.

[2] K. Watanabe and Y. Sumiyoshi, *Jnl. of Crystal Growth,* **24/25** (1975) 666.

[3] R. C. Linares, *Jnl. of Physics & Chemistry of Solids,* **26** (1965) 1817.

[4] A. B. Chase, *Jnl. of the American Ceramic Society,* **49** (1966) 233.

[5] H. J. Scheel & D. Elwell, *Jnl. of Crystal Growth,* **12** (1972) 153.

[6] H. J. Scheel, *Jnl. of Crystal Growth,* **13/14** (1972) 560.

[7] D. Elwell & H. J. Scheel, *Crystal Growth from High Temperature Solutions,* Academic Press, 1972.

Appendix 4

SUPPLIERS OF MAN-MADE GEMSTONES

Lists are given below of some manufacturers and retailers of synthetic gemstones. These are not comprehensive, but will provide a few addresses where lapidarists can write for rough, or which home jewellers can contact for facetted stones.

A   Manufacturers

Belgard & Frank Inc., 17 E 37th St., New York, NY 10016, USA (Cat's-eye substitute).

C. F. Chatham, 70 14th St., San Francisco, CA 94103, USA (emerald and ruby, normally to trade only).

Creative Crystals, PO Box 506, Danville, CA 94526, USA (alexandrite, trade only).

Crystal Technology Inc., 2510A Old Middlefield Way, Mountain View, CA 94041, USA (lithium niobate and lithium tantalate).

Deltronic Crystal Industries Inc., PO Box 323, Denville, NJ 07834, USA (ruby, sapphire, cubic zirconia, GGG, trade only).

Djevahirdjian SA, 1870 Monthey, Switzerland (corundum and spinel, star stones, cubic zirconia, usually sold to trade).

Empreza De Couto Trading Co., Jarvis Bdg., 75 Kyomachi, Ikuta-ku, Kobe, Japan (strontium titanate, sapphire doublet).

P. Gilson SA Lapidaires, Campagne/Wardrecques, 62120 Aire, France (emerald, coral, lapis lazuli, opal, turquoise).

ICT Inc., 1330 Industrial Drive, Shelby, MI 49455, USA (YAG in white, blue-white, aqua blue, dark blue, yellow, pink and green; GGG, cubic zirconia).

Iimori Laboratory, 1–7 Sugano 1-chome, Toshima-ku, Tokyo 170, Japan (jade simulant and man-made chatoyant, also lapis simulant).

Laser Technology Inc., 10624 Ventura Blvd., N. Hollywood, CA 91604, USA (strontium titanate – sapphire doublet).

Nakazumi Crystal Corp., Ikeda Hankyu Bldg., 2–1 Sakae-machi, Ikeda-shi, Osaka, Japan (star sapphire).

Rubis Synthetique des Alpes, 38-Jarrie, France (corundum and spinel).

Synthetic Crystal Products Corp., 154 Edison Rd., Lake Hopatcong, NJ 07849, USA (YAG, including a range of coloured stones, GGG).

B Dealers

A large number of dealers sell boules and cut stones of corundum and spinel, and most readers will find a retailer in their area. In case readers have problems, a few dealers who have extensive lists of synthetic gems, or particular specialities are listed below. (Apologies are due to the many dealers not included). The April issue of *Lapidary Journal* has an up-to-date list of dealers each year.

Atomergic Chemicals Corp., 100 Fairchild Ave., Plainview, NY 11803, USA (YAG, including coloured stones; lithium niobate; strontium titanate; emerald; GGG; corundum; spinel; rutile. including canary and blue boules and cut stones, minimum order $250).

Elvin, PO Box 787, Westfield, NJ 07090, USA (Linde star stones).

Hirsch Jacobson Co. Ltd., 91 Marylebone High St., London WIM 3DE, England (corundum, spinel, YAG, GGG).

Walter E. Johansen, PO Box 907, Morgan Hill, CA 95037, USA (corundum, spinel, blue and blue-green quartz, YAG [white, blue-white, green and lavender], GGG, strontium titanate, rutile, cubic zirconia; mail order specialist).

MDI Corp., 3417 Rochester Rd., Royal, MI 48073, USA (Slocum stone).

Shila-Art Gems Inc., 50 W 47th St., New York NY 10036, USA (corundum, spinel, star stones, Chatham emerald, 'Catseye', YAG, strontium titanate, strontium titanate/spinel doublets, GGG, cubic zirconia).

Transworld Trading Co., 565 Fifth Ave., New York NY 10017, USA (YAG, GGG, strontium titanate, Chatham emerald, cubic zirconia).

Appendix 5

BIBLIOGRAPHY

These books on gems in general, or on specific aspects, are listed here as suggestions for further reading or reference.

(1) M. O'Donoghue, *Synthetic Gem Materials,* Goldsmiths Co., London, 1976.
(2) D. MacInnes, *Synthetic Gem and Allied Crystal Manufacture,* Noyes Data Corp., 1971.
(3) Paul E. Desautels, *The Gem Kingdom,* Random House, New York, 1976.
(4) E. H. Rutland, *An Introduction to the World's Gemstones,* Hamlyn, 1974.
(5) R. Webster, *Gems,* Butterworth, 1970.
(6) G. F. Herbert Smith, *Gemstones,* Pitman, New York, 1958.
(7) J. L. Arem. *Gems and Jewelry,* Bantam, 1975.
(8) B. W. Anderson, *Gemstones for Everyman,* Faber, 1976.
(9) P. Bariand, *World Treasury of Minerals in Color,* Galahad, New York, 1976.
(10) E. Bruton, *Diamonds,* N.A.G. Press, 1970 (2nd Edition in preparation).
(11) J. L. Arem, *Man-Made Crystals,* Smithsonian Press, Washington, 1973.
(12) D. Elwell and H. J. Scheel, *Crystal Growth from High-Temperature Solutions,* Academic Press, London, 1975.

Index